# CQI AND THE RENOVATION OF AN AMERICAN HEALTH CARE SYSTEM

Also available from ASQ Quality Press

*The Handbook for Managing Change in Health Care*
Chip Caldwell, editor

*Mentoring Strategic Change in Health Care: An Action Guide*
Chip Caldwell

*The Effectiveness of CQI in Health Care: Stories from a Global Perspective*
Vahé Kazandjian, editor

*How to Lower Health Care Costs by Improving Health Care Quality: Results-Based Continuous Quality Improvement*
M. Daniel Sloan

*Success Stories on Lowering Health Care Costs by Improving Health Care Quality*
M. Daniel Sloan and Jodi B. Torpey

*The Quality Toolbox*
Nancy R. Tague

*Mapping Work Processes*
Dianne Galloway

*Understanding and Applying Value-Added Assessment: Eliminating Business Process Waste*
William E. Trischler

*The Change Agents' Handbook: A Survival Guide for Quality Improvement Champions*
David W. Hutton

To request a complimentary catalog of publications, call 800-248-1946.

# CQI AND THE RENOVATION OF AN AMERICAN HEALTH CARE SYSTEM

## A CULTURE UNDER CONSTRUCTION

Sister Mary Jean Ryan, FSM
William P. Thompson

ASQ Health Care Series
Chip Caldwell, editor

ASQ Quality Press
Milwaukee, Wisconsin

*CQI and the Renovation of an American Health Care System*
*A Culture Under Construction*
Sister Mary Jean Ryan, FSM, and William P. Thompson
ASQ Health Care Series    Chip Caldwell, editor

Library of Congress Cataloging-in-Publication Data
Ryan, Mary Jean, Sister, 1938–
    CQI and the renovation of an American health care system: a
culture under construction / Sister Mary Jean Ryan, William P.
Thompson.
        p.  cm. — (ASQ health care series)
    Includes bibliographical references and index.
    ISBN 0-87389-417-0 (alk. paper)
    1. Health services administration—United States.  2. Total
quality management—United States.  3. Organizational change—United
States.  4. SSM Health Care System (Saint Louis, Mo.).  I. Thompson,
William P., 1950–  .  II. Title.  III. Series.
RA971.R93   1997
362.1'0973—dc21                                                      97-3243
                                                                          CIP

10 9 8 7 6 5 4 3 2

ISBN 0-87389-417-0

Acquisitions Editor: Roger Holloway
Project Editor: Kelley Cardinal

ASQ Mission: To facilitate continuous improvement and increase customer satisfaction by identifying, communicating, and promoting the use of quality principles, concepts, and technologies; and
thereby be recognized throughout the world as the leading authority on, and champion for, quality.

*Attention: Schools and Corporations*
ASQ Quality Press books, videotapes, audiotapes, and software are available at quantity discounts
with bulk purchases for business, educational, or instructional use. For information, please contact
ASQ Quality Press at 800-248-1946, or write to ASQ Quality Press, P.O. Box 3005, Milwaukee, WI
53201-3005.

For a free copy of the ASQ Quality Press Publications Catalog, including ASQ membership
information, call 800-248-1946.

Printed in the United States of America

 Printed on acid-free paper

**American Society for Quality**

Quality Press
611 East Wisconsin Avenue
Milwaukee, Wisconsin 53202

Dedicated to
The Franciscan Sisters of Mary—
ever steadfast in their commitment
to quality health care

and to
all of the women and men associated
with the SSM Health Care System
whose work enlivens that commitment today
and ensures its continuation into the future.

The SSM Health Care System
has changed its name to SSM Health Care

# CONTENTS

# FOREWORD

Through my work in the quality movement, I have come to know a number of organizations that have taken the continuous quality improvement plunge. Some have found the water too cold and have turned back, heading to shore. Others have stuck with it, even when the going got tough.

I recall the first time I heard the pioneering scholar of quality, W. Edwards Deming, talk about "constancy of purpose" as his first principle; it seemed vague and obvious to me, and I wondered why he was spending so much time hammering at it. Over the years, I have come to know why. What it means is neither vague nor obvious, and we absolutely need clear, visible examples to remind us. This country has no better example than the SSM Health Care System.

This quality stuff is difficult, as Sister Mary Jean Ryan and Bill Thompson have found and describe eloquently in this book. But there is a real and palpable difference between those who are in it to ride the fad and those who are in it for the long haul because it is how they intend to lead their lives and their organizations. From the early days, the SSM Health Care System has been in that small, crucially important second group. I continue to admire the depth of commitment that Sister Mary Jean and her team have shown through thick and thin.

If you've opted for warmer, gentler water, or if you're madly treading water, take the time to read this book. It will soon become clear what constancy of purpose can mean to your organization and ultimately to our national community. As the SSM Health Care System has understood, a real commitment to improvement has the ability to touch the lives of thousands and thousands of people who will be better off in body and spirit.

Donald M. Berwick, M.D.
Institute for Healthcare Improvement
Boston, Massachusetts

# PREFACE

This book is about the SSM Health Care System's effort to transform itself into a culture where the continuous pursuit of excellence is simply "the way we work here."

Our purpose in writing it is to contribute something of what we have learned to executives and managers, in health care and elsewhere, who share a similar commitment to transforming their organizations. We believe that anyone willing to take on the task of implementing quality management—in any size organization—deserves to benefit from the experience, insights, and lessons of those who have gone before.

Since 1990, our entire system has been operating inside of the quality management framework known as continuous quality improvement (CQI). We were among the first health care systems to venture into quality improvement with a structured, comprehensive effort—constructing a new culture in unison, rather than as individual health care facilities.

Our corporate office vantage point has not permitted us to take in every detail or, thank God, to be involved in every decision regarding the quality improvement process in each facility. Some of what we relate here was shared with us by generous individuals at various locations in the system. It was often only through these conversations with colleagues and employees that we learned of the unheralded advocates of CQI who are working their way through cultural barriers and championing transformation beyond our line of sight.

Other aspects of the transformational process have been much more visible to us. CQI has accelerated the pace at which difficult questions regarding leadership and teamwork rise to the surface. Some issues, like fear in the workplace or labor unrest among nurses, are ones that we would have had to deal with in the 1990s regardless of whether we had chosen cultural transformation or the status quo. We believe that without the benefit of CQI's principles and processes, issues that could slow our system's progress would have taken longer to bring to light and address.

From the beginning, we have been inspired by the forerunners of the quality effort in health care, particularly Dr. Donald Berwick, who were always willing to share their knowledge and experience in the interest of improving American health care delivery. We committed ourselves to doing likewise.

Thus, in this book we share some things we would have done differently if we had known then what we know now. For example, we explain how we put too much early emphasis on process and not enough on accountability for measurable results in a specified period of time. We point out places where communication failed us. We also write about some pitfalls we stumbled into and corrections we have made along the way. And we acknowledge when we were just simply puzzled by the gaps between what we expected to happen and what actually happened.

We believe our experiences with CQI will be valuable especially to health care executives who are trying to implement quality improvements in large and diverse corporations. Our insights also may be useful for educators engaged in developing a new generation of professional health care managers.

Instilling the drive for continuous improvement within the variegated and complex environment of health care may be one of the most difficult efforts leaders and managers could undertake. It is our intention that the story of the SSM Health Care System's experience be of value to others who are working through the complexities to construct a new health care culture.

If one thing has given us the courage to share our missteps as well as successes, it is the confidence that we will eventually realize our vision of a cultural transformation within the SSM Health Care System. We offer this book with the hope that it contributes to your vision of such a transformation as well.

Sister Mary Jean Ryan, FSM
President and CEO

William P. Thompson
Senior Vice President—Strategic Development

# ACKNOWLEDGMENTS

So many people have contributed to our growth and learning in the world of continuous quality that we cannot identify or thank all of them here individually. We consider the men and women who have allowed us to learn from their efforts to implement CQI in health care, and other industries, to be pioneering heroes. They demonstrate their genuine commitment to quality not only by the work they do in their own organizations, but also by the generous sharing of their experiences with others.

Two of those whom we have had the privilege to work with more closely and learn from most significantly, we *must* mention by name. We thank Dr. Donald Berwick for undauntably pursuing the possibility of transforming American health care through quality improvement and for sharing his knowledge with us, both as a colleague and as a friend. We are grateful to Paul Plsek, who taught us much about the theory and practice of quality management and assisted us throughout our journey, especially in the early months as we designed the CQI curriculum and introduced our CQI plans throughout the system.

We also thank the people at Wainwright Industries, who have generously allowed the SSM Health Care System as a whole— as well as many of its individual managers—to benefit from Wainwright's experiences as a Malcolm Baldrige National Quality Award recipient.

We thank Chip Caldwell for recognizing our CQI efforts, for encouraging us early on to pursue the writing of this book, and for providing valuable feedback on the early drafts. We acknowledge Cathy Soete for providing research and editorial assistance in the development of the manuscript. In her work with us, Cathy demonstrated an extraordinary ability to grasp the nuances of our culture and the depth of our commitment to CQI.

Finally, we especially acknowledge the many women and men in the SSM Health Care System who so candidly shared with us their CQI experiences, accomplishments, and concerns so that we could benefit from their insights into this culture under construction.

# INTRODUCTION

To understand the enormous task the SSM Health Care System had in front of it when we took on the commitment to a cultural transformation through CQI, it is important to know something about its current status in American health care as well as its roots.

The SSM Health Care System, based in St. Louis, Missouri, is one of the largest Catholic health care systems in the country. It owns, operates, and manages 26 entities in Missouri, Wisconsin, Illinois, Oklahoma, South Carolina, and Georgia. The system has 21,750 employees and almost 5000 affiliated physicians working in direct care facilities (including 22 acute care hospitals) and related businesses. In 1994, it organized its St. Louis facilities into the St. Louis Health Care Network, an integrated delivery network composed of seven system-owned health centers, six affiliates, more than 3600 staff physicians, and a large array of programs and services.

The headquarters location has long been a center for health care delivery in the Midwest. A large number of free-standing sectarian and nonsectarian hospitals were established in the city of St. Louis in the early decades of the century. In the 1970s, several of them either moved to larger facilities in the surrounding suburbs or established annexes there. In the 1980s and early 1990s, many of these hospitals became part of sponsored health care systems. More recently, the most viable of these institutions, including those of the SSM Health Care System, have become members of integrated delivery networks.

The speed with which these consolidations occurred turned health care in the St. Louis metropolitan area, almost overnight, into an extremely competitive venture.

It is against this background, replicated to a lesser extent in other market areas, that the system management team and our institutions have been implementing continuous quality improvement.

## ROOTED IN VALUES

Although itself only 10 years old, the SSM Health Care System has had the inestimable benefit of a continuous, 125-year heritage of health care, passed on by the members of its sponsoring congregation. The Catholic religious community of health professionals was originally known as the Sisters of St. Mary. In the mid-1980s, as a result of reuniting with the Sisters of St. Francis of Maryville, the new congregation changed its name to the Franciscan Sisters of Mary. This reunification served to strengthen and enhance the sisters' commitment to providing health care to those in need.

Before 1985, most of the institutions that today belong to the SSM Health Care System were part of a group of hospitals owned by the sisters, centrally governed but having a decentralized management approach.

In the mid-1980s, as the result of a long-range planning process, the sponsoring congregation decided to reorganize its hospitals into a system of health care providers with a focus on centralized management. Out of this decision, the SSM Health Care System emerged, managed by a team of professional health care administrators—both lay and religious—and governed by members of the sponsoring congregation as well as laypersons from the communities served by our facilities.

A mission statement, as well as four principles and eight values, which our sponsoring congregation had recommitted itself to at the start of the 1980s, served as the foundation of the new system. Our mission is "To establish, maintain and enhance quality health services in accordance with our philosophy. We are committed to bring a comprehensive service approach to persons of all ages and social strata, with special concern for the poor."

These four principles serve as the cornerstones for the system's organizational structure.

1. *Collegiality*—Basing decisions on open communication, consensus, and cooperation

2. *Subsidiarity*—Making decisions at the point of greatest impact

3. *Collaboration*—Working with other individuals and institutions in the community toward common goals

4. *Accountability*—Taking responsibility for decisions and measuring outcomes against clear criteria

We created a system philosophy statement that includes these eight values.

1. Act with justice and fairness.
2. Give primary importance to those we serve.
3. Provide competent and caring service.
4. Change with the times to serve those in greatest need.
5. Promote in ourselves and others optimal function of body, mind, and spirit.
6. Foster communication, collaboration, and networking.
7. Generate a growth-producing climate.
8. Cultivate a community spirit.

Besides these eight foundational values, the system management team early on adopted the preservation of the earth, the practice of nonviolence, and respect for diversity as three other integral values of the system. As part of our commitment to nonviolence, our institutions have adopted the practice of eliminating language that connotes violent actions or attitudes wherever we become aware of it. In writing this book, we have tried to avoid expressions such as *target, capture, aim, hitting the mark,* and *cutting edge,* and instead use nonviolent language.

Perhaps another group of professionals assembled to manage the system's strategic planning, finance, and operations might have been happy to leave the foundational documents of the system hanging on the boardroom walls for inspiration while everyone got down to business. But this team of managers, the two of us included, was confronted by the fact that the values we espoused had no means of measurement in the field. While the system's philosophy was broadly communicated to employees and physicians, we weren't confident that anyone—including the team itself—regarded those statements as sacred promises to be kept.

All of our hospitals and other facilities had only recently been brought together as a system. They had had many years' head start implanting their own practices, history, and cultural traditions. Inside of the American Catholic hospital culture, there was also the culture of the religious congregation, the culture of each local community, the culture of physicians, and the culture of the individual facilities. Every entity of the system was laden with layers of routine practices passed on from one generation of managers, supervisors, and employees to the next.

At the start of its tenure, the system management team used a variety of conventional means to convey our mission and values, including newsletters, memos, new employee orientations, retreat days, leadership conferences, speeches, and so on. Administrative councils, made up of a president and several vice presidents at each facility, were charged with putting these values into practice.

For all of these efforts, however, we had no operational structures or consistent management processes to ensure that these values were being acted on every day in every department of every entity. The idealism of the system's values, while genuinely respected, didn't stand a chance next to the practical realities of habit, custom, and expediency.

Our traditional management practices and predominantly good intentions had allowed our hospitals to maintain an acceptable reputation and a relatively high level of care. But in our system management meetings, we realized that the mission of "continually enhancing quality" was chiding us to do more than we were doing— more than we already knew how to do.

The basic question that compelled us to go beyond traditional and familiar approaches was: What would it take to have the fulfillment of our mission, principles, and values be an everyday, commonplace reality? What would it take to have the continual enhancement of quality simply be the way we work here?

In the first two chapters of this book, we describe our original vision for continuous quality improvement and the pursuit of excellence as a blueprint for cultural transformation. We also give a brief overview of how we designed the structures we would use to implement CQI. (A more detailed look at some elements of CQI is provided in the appendix.) In chapters 3 through 8 we share some of the ups and downs of our CQI implementation, specifically in areas critical to the quality of our care and service for patients and other customers. And in chapter 9, we revisit the vision we created in 1990 and address some of the critical health care issues to be positively impacted by a culture of continuous improvement.

1

# BREAKING GROUND

*The year leading up to the SSM Health Care System's imple-mentation of continuous quality improvement (CQI) began with a vague discontent and turned into a time of intense research, thinking, and planning. The ultimate outcome was an all-out commitment to a systemwide cultural transformation.*

•••••••••••••••••••••••••••••••

As we sat in the sunshine of Marco Island, Florida, on a Saturday afternoon in mid-May 1989, what reason could we have to be discontent? Our annual system leadership conference had just come to a successful conclusion. And now we had a little time to relax and look ahead to what was next.

Even though the SSM Health Care System had gone through a few rough years financially, it had rebounded nicely and we now felt the system was well positioned for the future. We had recently divested three hospitals in Missouri that had been struggling for survival. And although the difficult decision wasn't universally welcomed, we were confident that it had put the entire system on a sound financial footing. The remaining facilities in the system had strong administrators, and the institutions themselves were generally recognized for providing high-quality care and high levels of satisfaction.

Yet even as we felt a sense of accomplishment, we also felt a vague discontent.

Both of us knew that the system's greatest strength is that it is a values-driven organization. We believed that if the leaders within the system communicated those values and consistently challenged people to live up to them, there would be no limits to the excellence of our care and service.

As we talked that afternoon in 1989, though, we realized that no matter how much we communicated the system's vision and values, some things were just not happening. We didn't see a constant striving for improvement. We didn't see managers mobilizing the people around them to work on projects that were important. And we didn't see processes in place to truly make the best use of people's talents.

We had developed competence in producing thoughtful leadership conferences that conveyed powerful themes based on our vision and values. The theme of the just-completed conference had been "Servant Leadership," based on Robert Greenleaf's book of the same name.[1] In the talks and workshop sessions, participants had been encouraged to create a climate of listening and to empower employees to develop themselves as partners in the system's mission.

Servant leadership had seemed a logical progression from our 1988 conference on intrapreneurship, suggested by Gifford Pinchot's book about organizational entrepreneurs.[2] The group of leaders at that conference had been challenged to support employees in taking initiative and making improvements in their work.

But as we looked toward the 1990 leadership conference, we both knew that something else was needed. We had gleaned good ideas from management thinkers in previous years, but we had to reach further. Inspiring themes are not enough to ensure the pursuit of excellence.

In a moment of brainstorming, Sister Mary Jean said she wanted to learn more about the work of Brent James, director of medical research of Intermountain Health Care in Salt Lake City, Utah. She had heard his presentation earlier that year on the statistical evaluation of clinical processes.[3] James had told of surgeons changing some of their practice patterns when they saw objective data about variations in their surgical processes and results. Those changes resulted in reduced variation, greater efficiency, and lower costs.

Coincidentally, Bill had been reading about process variation inside of the larger topic of quality management. He wanted to find out if the quality theories were as applicable to health care as they were to manufacturing.

We left Marco Island ready to research a new direction. We had no idea that we had already reached a turning point that Saturday afternoon.

## CONNECTING CQI WITH PATIENT CARE

The goal of quality is to understand what the customer wants and then meet or exceed those wants by designing and redesigning processes to continuously improve the product.

The quality movement had been imported back to America from Japan because U.S. manufacturing companies belatedly recognized that the consumers of cars, appliances, parts, and equipment were the ones to satisfy. The job was to keep refining the process so that customers would get more of what they wanted.

At first, though, the link between quality theories and health care wasn't as easy to see. In a field where practitioners think of their work in personal and professional terms, it seemed odd to refer to health care as a product, the work of doctors and nurses as a repeatable process, and patients as customers.

The complexity of health care also raised a question. Could quality management succeed in the clinical arena, where professional, technical, and skilled and unskilled workers have multiple categories of customers?

For example, a nurse trying to meet the quality goal would have to first understand and then meet or exceed the needs of the person receiving the care; other people giving care—primary care physician, specialist, therapist, and social worker; people concerned about the patient—relatives and friends; and people accountable for medical records, discharge planning, and patient accounts. In addition, all of the nurse's customers would have their own intermingled sets of customers—dietitians, housekeeping personnel, security guards, parking lot attendants, building engineers, EMTs, and so on.

This virtually endless loop of overlapping processes, carried out 24 hours a day, seven days a week, across various reporting structures and lines of accountability and within different departments, floors, wings, and—for larger health care enterprises—separate buildings, seemed enough to make continuous quality improvement unattainable. Yet it was exactly the process-focused character of quality management that appealed to us most as we looked for a way to weave the system's values into all of its operations.

We began to believe that continuous quality improvement was a possibility worth pursuing. After all, if a single physician had been able to improve outcomes by using one process measurement tool in a surgical department, what improvements might the SSM Health Care System reap by using many of them in all of its entities?

## MEETING SOME QUALITY THINKERS

In early summer of 1989, Bill and Vito Tamboli (a now-retired system vice president) attended a three-day seminar on quality principles in health care put on by the National Demonstration Project (NDP) for Quality Improvement in Health Care.[4] The NDP had paired 35 health care organizations with local businesses that were using CQI principles. The purpose was to see if the quality principles could be applied in those health institutions.

The seminar was our first contact with professionals who were using quality principles in health care delivery. Here we also met Paul Plsek, a consultant and course instructor, whom we later hired to guide us through mountains of quality theory.

By late summer, our advance team, consisting of Bill, Vito, and Gayle Capozzalo (then senior vice president for strategic development), had convinced the rest of system management that we should pursue quality management soon and seriously. We moved quickly, bringing in Plsek for three day-long sessions in September and November 1989 and January 1990, to help us develop an implementation plan. In these sessions, he outlined the CQI structures that we eventually adapted and adopted for the SSM Health Care System.

To expose our entities' management teams and the system's leading physicians to the concepts of quality improvement, we held an additional conference in October with Plsek, Brent James, and W. H. Bruning of the Process Management Institute (PMI).

While James provided evidence that quality management could make a difference on the clinical side of health care, Donald Berwick (then with the Harvard Community Health Plan) provided a theoretical background.

# TWO IDEAS THAT CHALLENGED THE OLD PARADIGM

In clinical matters, we already had a process orientation. Diagnosis, medications, surgery, and therapeutic treatments all require health professionals to follow certain steps and to reference the patient's chart, heart monitor, X-rays, laboratory tests, and other objective data as a matter of course.

Yet in most other areas of our entities, hundreds of processes that affect timeliness, accuracy, economy, service, and convenience were in no way being evaluated on the basis of objective data. And without either the data or the systematic means to gather them, opinions, "gut feelings," personal preferences, and styles were all given undeserved weight.

We learned two theories of continuous improvement that helped us begin breaking ground for a new culture. One was the Theory of Bad Apples.

## Theory of Bad Apples

This theory is described in a Berwick article in the *The New England Journal of Medicine*.[5] The idea is that health care quality is not improved by inspecting for "bad apples" and removing them from the barrel.

The pursuit of quality by inspection shows up in health care as obligatory recertification or as "deterrence." The theory implicitly suggests that quality will be determined by someone who judges, after the fact, whether or not a product or service crossed the boundaries of acceptability. Such things as mortality data, case mix, and the findings of regulators are used as evidence.

It wasn't hard for us to see that when health care quality is defined by the presence or absence of an official stamp of acceptability, the desire to pursue excellence either dissipates or becomes focused somewhere else. We have, unfortunately, heard the statement "Our ratings are as good or better than others" used many times as a justification for the status quo.

The bad apple theory can be applied to employees, as well. When people realize they are working in a culture that is trying to rid itself of bad apples, they become defensive and use their energy trying to prove that they are not one. In such a culture, employees at all levels have adversarial relationships with their supervisors or managers. As a measure of protection, these employees feel they have to distort, deny or justify data, or blame others.

Berwick, following the quality theories of industry, was proposing that the overall level of quality in clinical practice had much more to do with processes than with people. He said that quality could be improved when managers created systems for employees to measure process variation, share data about the impact of that variation, and redesign or newly design processes so as to control the variation that causes poor or unreliable outcomes.

In light of the SSM Health Care System's value of acting with justice and fairness and our heritage of Catholic social teaching regarding the dignity of workers, we always considered it important to regard employees in our system as caring and well intentioned. The bad apple theory made clear to us, however, that even when we thought we were being compassionate and understanding in evaluating people, we were still focusing on the wrong thing.

The theory of continuous improvement, when contrasted with the theory of bad apples, gave us access to the real source of quality problems *and* quality improvement: the process itself.

## The Parable of the Red Beads

W. Edwards Deming's demonstration, called the Parable of the Red Beads, brought home to us an essential understanding of the pervasiveness of variation in processes. The parable uses the fictional White Bead Company to demonstrate the problems that are caused when process variations—in this case, the production of some red beads—are incorrectly interpreted and ineffectively acted on.

In the parable, the manager tries to eliminate process variation rather than determine if it exceeds the range of random variation that occurs in any process. The manager's impulse to do something about variation results in fruitless efforts to improve, motivate, or browbeat the workers, leading to the company's failure.

The Parable of the Red Beads left us with an indelible lesson in the principles of variation. Before any process can be improved, the people designing or redesigning it must be able to interpret the variation accurately, measure it, and distinguish whether it is a common cause or a special cause variation. Only then can a decision be made about the best action to take.

In a hospital, for example, the time needed to efficiently and effectively prepare an operating room for surgery will vary within a range of minutes. The process will be affected by a variety of common causes. As long as the process happens in a certain range of minutes, and the identified cause is common to the process, no action needs to be taken.

A second key lesson in the parable was that people's performance is truly a function of the processes with which they work, not a reflection of the individuals' good or bad intentions. To make a significant change, it is essential to focus on improving the processes people are using.

As the system management team continued its research, we saw that focusing on process variation, analyzing its causes, and designing or redesigning processes would be a measurable way to carry out our mission to "establish, maintain and enhance quality."

While we were learning about the practical tools of measurement and analysis, Plsek recommended that we also articulate the key principles that would serve as the foundation for implementing CQI throughout our system. We selected five principles that we believed would be the spring from which our entire CQI implementation could flow (see Figure 1.1).

## COMMITTING TO A CULTURAL REVOLUTION

Articulating our CQI principles sealed our resolve about pursuing continuous quality improvement. We recognized that the principles, both in content and philosophy, echoed the eight values of the SSM Health Care System.

Our system's values undeniably come from a Catholic tradition, and it seemed particularly appealing to us that the CQI principles

---

1. Patients and other customers are our first priority.

2. Quality is achieved through people.

3. All work is part of a process.

4. Decision making is done by facts.

5. Quality requires continuous improvement.

---

**Figure 1.1.** CQI principles.

were so compatible with our heritage. Yet we have to note that the simple reality of CQI is that *anyone* can follow its principles without concern for being Catholic, Christian, or anything at all religious. The CQI philosophy has universal breadth.

It was difficult for anyone in system management to argue against something that was so consistent with our values. Although two team members did express some reticence about launching into such a large endeavor, by the time we were ready to make the yes-or-no decision, every person at the conference table could give his or her approval.

Through the fall of 1989, members of the system management team and individuals from the administrative councils of our entities visited companies and institutions that were committed to quality management. In addition, we continued reading, sharing articles with each other, and endlessly planning.

The CQI plans, while detailed, were highly conceptual, providing only the vaguest sense of what we were actually taking on. Designing the phases, the schedule, and the education curriculum with Paul Plsek was like working with an architect's rendering. On paper, you can reassign the spaces and reposition plumbing and wiring with ease. Working with the real thing, you have to bear the consequences of delays, change orders, mistakes, and bad weather.

We were still in the stage where we could redesign elements of the CQI implementation. Having to deal with our actual ways of working lay ahead. The closer we moved toward implementation, the clearer the extent of the effort became to us. We said over and over again to ourselves and each other that this was not going to be some "program" we were concocting to try out for a while and see what would happen. We were committing to a systemic change for our entire enterprise, one that would affect our future in ways we could not predict.

We were adamant that CQI not be perceived as a project that an outside consultant or one staff member would handle for us. We vowed there would never be a person "in charge of quality improvement." To cause the kind of change we imagined, we would have to bring people along at every step. Ultimately, no one could afford to be left out of the information and education process.

Our decision to include the clinical as well as administrative aspects of our facilities was an early and important one. We had a physician on the implementation team for about the first six months of phase one.

In addition, by including leading physicians from our facilities in the initial October 1989 meeting with the presidents and system management, we hoped to create a cadre of physicians who would support the concept of quality improvement among their colleagues in the facilities. Over the following months, we actively sought physicians' opinions and input about what we were developing and what they thought the barriers might be.

Our January 1990 conference for hands-on healers was the first broad unveiling of our quality plans. "Hands-on healers" was our name for a select group of people from throughout the organization who give direct or indirect patient care and who have no management or supervisory responsibility. Each year, for about seven years, facilities were asked to send to the hands-on healers conference a cadre of people who, in the presidents' estimation, lived out the SSM Health Care System values. Over four days, with outside speakers designated for different groups, we informed this select group of physicians, nurses, technicians, social workers, and sisters from the sponsoring congregation about the CQI initiative.

At one point, someone in a group of employees asked, "Who's responsible for this concept?" Sister Mary Jean, with tongue in cheek, responded, "If you like it, I am. If you don't, then we all made the decision." Then, just as quickly, she pointed out that system management worked as a team and had made the decision as a team. One of the participants said, "We really like it." With that, the whole group spontaneously stood and applauded.

That was one of those early moments in CQI when we sensed we were launching something that people could get excited about. The management team members breathed a collective sigh of relief that, on this leg of our CQI "road show," the early reviews were good.

This affirmation came from a key group—people who were at the front line in each of our facilities, providing direct or indirect care to patients. Their response to CQI heartened us as we went through the next four months of intensive work preceding the official rollout of the implementation plan at our May 1990 SSM leadership conference.

## CULTURAL TRANSFORMATION BEGINS TO SINK IN

Although creating the plan was a huge task, the more demanding job was preparing ourselves for the changes we would have to make. We could not simply distribute an implementation document for others to try out while we observed the results from the corporate office. If we were to lead the system's cultural transformation, we had to be willing to question our own ways of working.

Long before we had committed to CQI, Sister Mary Jean had advocated a reassessment of health care delivery. Despite all the evidence in government and society that the old ways of delivering care were no longer adequate, many inside the industry continued to hold onto the past.

Methods of running hospitals; talking to and taking care of patients; ordering tests; hiring, firing, and working with employees; communicating across department lines; and interacting with the myriad users of a hospital's facilities had all been inherited from an earlier era. It was an era of generous reimbursement, apparently unlimited resources, and patriarchal doctor-patient relationships. Now, even though circumstances had drastically changed, many otherwise bright people were still holding onto the same administrative and clinical practices.

All of us in system management came to see that we had been tolerating the same kinds of inefficient processes, or lack of processes, that were creating waste and rework in health care facilities. That wasn't surprising, considering that we each came to our jobs either through clinical supervisory posts or hospital management, bringing our work habits with us.

Bright, educated people who want to make a difference in their field quickly adopt the ways of the pervasive culture or paradigm so that they can get things done. They become leaders and, in turn, perpetuate the paradigm.

Paul Plsek pointed out that many of us on the system management team exhibited the traits of two heroic characters in our work styles. The Lone Rangers among us typically come to our work confident that we can accomplish what we need to accomplish if other people just leave us alone and let us handle things. Some of us prefer the role of Mighty Mouse, who flies in to save the day by doing other people's jobs, solving other people's problems, or averting catastrophe at the last moment.

In early conversations with Plsek and among ourselves, we began to uncover the heroic views we had of ourselves. And later, in reading Peter Senge's book *The Fifth Discipline,*[6] we realized that operating out of a particular perspective or "mental model" was something that everyone does—whether it is acknowledged or not.

But the possibility of radically altering our ways of managing and delivering health care was compelling to those of us who felt that many things about health care were in need of a cure.

We would have a mountain of educating to do on the critical issue of our ultimate purpose in implementing CQI. We anticipated then, and our anticipation proved correct, that inside of the tumultuous state of the health care industry there would be skepticism and cynicism about our motives for change.

Some personnel would perceive CQI as simply an elaborate cost reduction measure in sheep's clothing. And some would see it as an expensive and tedious exercise that would eventually be swept aside for another management fad or, more cynically put, another "flavor of the month." For these, as well as for the many employees and physicians in between, we would need to find ways to thoroughly inform and educate about the long-range possibilities of CQI.

## COST REDUCTION AS A MEASURABLE RESULT, NOT A MOTIVATION FOR CQI

When U.S. manufacturing companies were forced to become more competitive in the global marketplace, decreasing the costs of production and increasing the productivity of workers were seen as two ways to do that. Managing for quality had proved to be measurably successful in saving production dollars for many reasons. The act of analyzing and improving key production processes saves money because there is less material waste, less rework, less overtime, and higher productivity, because the job is more often being done "right the first time, every time."

As price competition and reimbursement limits hit the health care industry with a vengeance, cost reduction became an imperative for hospitals, too. Many of the institutions we had visited had been motivated to implement quality management efforts by the promise that improving processes promotes cost containment.

Research had shown that improving quality in a health care setting did indeed lead to lower costs, especially in the areas of waste reduction and productivity. Brent James' *Quality Management for Health Care Delivery*[7] cited estimated potential savings ranging from 20 percent to 40 percent of total health care outlays when the two areas of waste and productivity are spotlighted.

Our system certainly had no argument with the cost savings aspect of a quality effort. Hospitals were undeniably guilty of wasting vast amounts of time, supplies, materials, and energy. Waste is always the cost culprit in health care, and quality improvement directly impacts waste.

Even though we fully expected that cost containment would be an eventual and natural result of improved processes, the system management team was emphatic about two key points: One, we would make no projections or promises about impacts to the bottom line. And two, cost reduction was not our rationale for implementing CQI.

In bringing system personnel into the conversation about CQI, we wanted to make sure this was clear. CQI was to be a structure for operationalizing our values, leading to the transformation of our entire organization.

## STARTING AT THE TOP

Through our conversations with others who had already begun the quality effort, we knew that our leadership had to be visible. The system management team took a hands-on approach to everything related to CQI from the very start.

At first, we called ourselves the CQI steering team. Soon, however, we saw that having two different names for the same group of people ran counter to our intention of having CQI fully incorporated with our way of working. Thus, we dropped the steering team designation.

In fall of 1989, we formed a larger implementation team, composed not only of system management but also a few of the entity presidents and a physician who, for a time, also served as the CQI corporate director of quality affairs. Paul Plsek served as the consultant to the team.

By expanding the leadership group when we did, we hoped to provide several advantages.

1. Early and direct participation by entity leaders would reflect the same degree of commitment at the local level as at the corporate level.

2. The increased involvement of key leaders would give greater credibility and visibility to the effort, both critical factors.

3. The wider spectrum of viewpoints, experiences, and insights—including the clinical perspective—would help to shape a more real-world plan and provide a preview of people's concerns, barriers, and objections.

4. The learning/research capability of the team was extended.

5. Not unimportantly, the workload was distributed over a larger number of people.

## SPELLING OUT CQI FOR THE BOARD OF DIRECTORS

The system's board of directors earlier had approved a strategic plan containing the requirement that every entity always be working toward the improvement of quality, in accord with the mission statement. Having that charge as part of our strategic plan meant that the system management team already had the authority to specifically determine how that objective would be fulfilled.

Only after the team voted to go forward with CQI did we bring the plan to the board members. Bill was chosen to give an informational presentation to the 10-member board in February 1990.

CQI was a totally new concept for most of the board members, and Bill came prepared to explain its principles and processes in detail. As the board listened, about half of the members seemed open and accepting of what Bill had to say. Other members, though, seemed skeptical and expressed misgivings.

Generally, their concerns were that CQI came out of a manufacturing context and would bring too commercial an attitude to health care and service. There was doubt that patients, referred to in CQI as "customers," could be trusted to judge quality in health care. Some members said that CQI seemed too mechanical and that they could not see where the system's values fit in.

By the end of the meeting with the board, which had not gone as well as we had hoped, our eyes were opened to the assumption we had made. During the presentation, the close relationship between the CQI principles and the system's values was referred to but not articulated in so many words. We expected the board to see the connection between CQI's principles and the SSM Health Care System's values as readily as we had. The unpersuaded board members, however, wanted to see the relationship explicitly.

A short time after that board meeting, the system management team met for one of its periodic retreats. There, we broke into three groups and did a 20-minute exercise—probably the shortest process we've ever done. The result was a side-by-side comparison of the SSM Health Care System's eight values and CQI principles. When we brought a display of these values and principles back to the board in May 1990, all of the directors understood what we had seen in CQI (see Table 1.1).

**Table 1.1.** Link between SSM Health Care System values and CQI principles.

| SSM Values | CQI Principles |
|---|---|
| Act with fairness and justice. | All work is part of a process. Quality is achieved through people. Decision making is done by facts. |
| Give primary importance to those we serve. | Patients and other customers are our first priority. Quality is achieved through people. |
| Provide competent and caring service. | Patients and other customers are our first priority. |
| Change with the times to serve those in greatest need. | Patients and other customers are our first priority. Quality requires continuous improvement. |
| Promote in ourselves and others optimal function of body, mind, and spirit. | Quality is achieved through people. |
| Foster communication, collaboration, and networking. | All work is part of a process. Decision making is done by facts. Quality is achieved through people. |
| Generate a growth-producing climate. | Quality is achieved through people. |
| Cultivate a community spirit. | All work is part of a process. Decision making is done by facts. Quality is achieved through people. |

# THE PARALLELS BETWEEN OUR VALUES AND CQI PRINCIPLES

Our first value of acting with justice and fairness is fostered by CQI's method of decision making by objective data.

By design, the teams in each facility would first be trained in and then begin to use flowcharts, cause-and effect diagrams, run charts, histograms, scatter diagrams, and control charts. The information gained permits employees to set priorities for problem solving and pinpoint areas in a process where controls are needed and where variation can be reduced. People aren't penalized for faulty processes over which they have no control. With CQI, the burden of quality is on identifiable and traceable processes that have been designed or redesigned by people who use them every day.

Our second value is to give primary importance to those we serve. CQI supports this by providing the tools to measure processes and analyze how well we consistently deliver service to patients and our other customers.

The third value of providing competent and caring service is promoted by CQI's ever-present challenge to find ways to improve processes.

Our fourth and seventh values are closely related in CQI terms. The fourth value is to change with the times to serve those in greatest need; the seventh is to generate a growth-producing climate. CQI necessitates the ongoing education of employees and supports the open and flexible management style that both of these values require. In an environment where there are ongoing opportunities to analyze what can be improved and to design new ways to work, there is a greater spirit of innovation an sense of ownership.

CQI also supports our fifth value—to promote the optimal function of body, mind, and spirit in ourselves and others. Continuous improvement in health care rarely relies on sophisticated technology, but rather on managers and employees putting their personal talents and resources to better use. The skills needed to do this encompass all aspects of a person, from physical well-being to creative thinking, teamwork, and camaraderie.

Our sixth value—to foster communication, collaboration, and networking—is both supported and tested by CQI. Its entire structure relies on a willingness to relate, cooperate, and work together.

The teamwork needed to solve problems and design new processes can't happen without those three skills.

Regarding our eighth value—to cultivate a community spirit—CQI enhances this commitment by its emphasis on common ownership of goals, results, and accomplishments.

For the system management team, the side-by-side arrangement was not as important as the fact that there was an overall correlation of the CQI spirit and principles to the SSM Health Care System values. Yet we learned an early lesson from our board of directors: A key part of educating people about CQI would be going beyond our assumptions and spelling things out clearly and completely.

We felt, based on the board's concern, that not everyone would be as quick to see the comparison between CQI and our values. The side-by-side diagram of values and principles, therefore, was placed at the front of the introductory material in our CQI implementation manual and was used as a key tool in the CQI educational process with system personnel.

## A WORD ABOUT LOCAL BOARDS

As we gathered information from health care institutions that operate with local boards of directors, we realized that our system's more centralized management and governance structure gave us greater freedom to act quickly on CQI.

In most of the communities where we operate a hospital or other health facility, local residents serve on advisory boards to provide input and support for the institution's activities. These boards do not have the authority to approve hiring or spending decisions.

Hospitals or other health care facilities governed by boards that have the authority to affirm or deny a major commitment of funds, staff time, or other resources clearly face a lengthier education process regarding the implementation of a quality improvement effort.

The customary, and valid, questions from board members about how much money, how much time before bottom-line results are seen, and so on would be difficult, if not impossible, to answer. From our perspective, it would take an inspired educational process to be able to move a local board swiftly beyond these questions, especially because continuous improvement does not offer quick, tangible results.

In the traditional way of operating, a board that does not have those bottom-line questions answered to its satisfaction would be more likely to say "Forget it" than "Proceed."

## TEN TIPS TO CONSIDER DURING THE PLANNING STAGE OF CQI

1. Regardless of how well your organization is doing in comparison to others in your market area, you need to be absolutely convinced that everything can be done better. If you are satisfied with the status quo, you won't have the heart to go through what it takes to implement quality management.

2. No matter how much you would prefer to have a committee "just handle" the quality management implementation, there's no chance of it happening successfully if top executives are not actively engaged.

3. A trusted consultant who has already explored the quality terrain won't spare you all of the mistakes and missteps, but he or she can save you a lot of time and duplication of effort at the beginning.

4. If you see quality improvement as a good motivational campaign for your employees, we recommend that you reconsider the whole idea.

5. Approaching quality improvement as a cost-cutting measure will doom it to failure as a means of transforming the culture of your organization.

6. Including opinion leaders—from all levels—early in the process of change is a necessary, but not sufficient, condition of success. Just inviting people to meetings and copying them on reports doesn't guarantee their advocacy or action. But by *not* doing so, you almost guarantee that they will not speak or act in favor of quality efforts. We found that the positive opinion leaders were the ones who worked on a team project and got to see the results of their work firsthand.

7. If there isn't information from sources who can speak with authority, somebody will make stuff up. The made-up news creates rumors, worry, and often resentment.

8. Once you become immersed in the subject of quality, you may tend to forget that not everyone is so immersed. Assuming that people know or understand quality management is a risky business. Informational meetings, graphic displays (for example, our values/principles display for the board members), videos, newsletters, Q&A sessions, and so on provide people with accurate information and sometimes—but not always—allay their concerns.

9. If you intend to include clinical aspects in the quality improvement effort, physicians should participate in the planning conversations and their perspectives should be sought out and listened to. Not getting all of the physician support you would like isn't a reason to stop. Some physicians will buy in only after they see evidence that it works.

10. It is counterproductive to create separate entities, special units, or anything to suggest that CQI stands alone from the institution's operating structure. New committees, teams,

offices, and positions may have to be created, but they should be integrated just the same as would any new function, with established accountabilities and lines of reporting.

*The system management team moved decisively to put CQI into motion after it became clear that quality management could be applied to health care. The driving intention was not cost savings, but rather the desire to integrate the system's values into every process.*

## Notes

1. Robert K. Greenleaf, *Servant Leadership* (Ramsey, N.J.: Paulist Press, 1977).

2. Gifford Pinchot III, *Intrapreneuring* (New York: Harper & Row, 1985).

3. Brent James, talk delivered at American Hospital Association Conference, March 1989.

4. National Demonstration Project for Quality Improvement in Health Care, funded by the John A. Hartford Foundation and The Harvard Community Health Plan Foundation, organized by Donald Berwick, M.D., and A. Blanton Godfrey, Ph.D.

5. Donald Berwick, "Continuous Improvement as an Ideal in Health Care," *The New England Journal of Medicine* (January 5, 1989).

6. Peter Senge, *The Fifth Discipline* (New York: Doubleday Currency, 1990), 8.

7. Brent James, *Quality Management for Health Care Delivery* (Salt Lake City, Utah: Intermountain Health Care, 1989).

2

# LAYING
# THE
# FOUNDATION

*Just one year after our first conversation about quality management, we were launching CQI systemwide. This chapter describes the foundational elements of our plan and the initial issues we had to clarify for employees of the system.*

. . . . . . . . . . . . . . . . . . . . . . . . . . . . . . .

On May 10, 1990, Sister Mary Jean officially began a new era in the SSM Health Care System. Her purpose was to lay out the entire CQI plan to 200 of the system's key leaders from our health facilities, corporate office, and sponsoring congregation.

31

The SSM Health Care System was committing a budget of more than half a million dollars for the first year alone of CQI implementation, with no guarantees. We couldn't promise that after the money allotted for CQI was spent and the time for its full integration into the system had arrived, CQI would be a success. The outcome depended on people at every level committing themselves to the possibility of a new way of working in a new organization (see Table 2.1). People would have to be willing to learn the tools of objective measurement and analysis and use those tools to design and redesign the processes of their jobs.

To generate the momentum needed to sustain a long-range effort, we needed to raise enthusiasm for CQI at this leadership

**Table 2.1.** The new organization: Changes in management perspective.

| Old Way | New Way |
|---|---|
| Quality is fine. | Quality can and must be improved. |
| Poor quality and defects come from people. | Poor quality and defects come from complex processes. |
| Checking and data reporting, exhorting people, and giving incentives ensure quality. | Analysis and understanding of processes ensure quality. |
| Use intuition and the latest technology to address problems. | Collect data and act with knowledge to address problems. |
| Improvement must occur within functional areas. | Improvement must occur among functional areas as well as within them. |
| Customers are problems. | Customers are partners. |
| Suppliers are problems. | Suppliers are partners. |
| Quality costs money. | Quality saves money. |
| We don't have time to improve quality. | We don't have time not to improve quality. |

conference and also present a tangible structure that would elevate CQI beyond "this year's theme." We altered the usual structure of the conference, forgoing an outside keynote speaker.

Sister Mary Jean not only unveiled the concept and motivation for CQI, but also graphically presented the nuts and bolts of the schedule, budget, reporting process, team structures, and other concrete elements needed to anchor the vision of continuous improvement in reality.

Members of the system management team had written the CQI manual, which outlined the entire three-phase implementation plan. Our ultimate intention, which we believed would take five years or more to achieve, was to so instill the drive for continuous quality in the culture of our organization that CQI, as a distinct concept, would be indiscernible. As Sister Mary Jean would say, "'CQI' would disappear and in its place would be simply 'the way we work here.'"

## THE THREE PHASES OF CQI

The three-phase, five-year plan for CQI was an act of faith. With no history to go on, a year-long pilot project would have been much safer.

Phase I, Quality Improvement Teams, was slated to take two years to implement systemwide. This would be a massive educational and team-building effort during which employees at every level, as well as physicians, would be trained in CQI principles and tools of measurement and analysis so that they could design processes or solve process problems.

Phase II, Quality Policy and Planning, was scheduled for 1992 to 1994. In this phase, the board of directors and system management would integrate CQI with system policy development and strategic planning.

Phase III, Quality in Daily Work Life, was scheduled to begin in 1994, with individual employees and physicians applying the CQI model to their everyday work.

On paper, the process for implementation seemed straight-forward enough. But in practice, we knew that everyone in the system would be like an infant learning to walk—putting one foot in front of the other and trying not to land too hard when we stumbled.

## BASICS OF PHASE I

The foundation of phase I was the CQI curriculum. In our site vis-its to quality management organizations, we had seen how critical awareness and education was for the people on the first quality improvement teams. Some organizations, in order to alleviate skepticism or produce quick results, had bypassed the education stage and moved into teams and projects before employees were ready.

We had decided that phase I would focus on all employees hav-ing the opportunity to take the necessary CQI courses before they served on a quality improvement teams (QIT). The first QITs would be assigned projects by their entity steering team or the sys-tem management team. When a project was completed, the team would dissolve.

Permanent teams could form later at the option of groups of employees who wanted to identify their own projects in a particular department or across several departments of a facility. The steering team would approve their projects and monitor their progress.

We knew it would take several years for everyone to participate in CQI classes. Even to get a few teams up and running at each entity would take more than a year. This lag time between CQI's introduction and the day when every employee was actively using the skills and tools of quality management posed a predictable problem. It would be difficult to maintain enthusiasm when the majority of people in the system could not participate immediately. Yet we believed that doing too much too fast at the outset could be detrimental, for two reasons.

First, it seemed impractical to try simultaneous startups at every facility, given the number of course leaders that would take. We wanted the system management team and entity leaders to serve as the first teachers of the CQI courses. This would give them a driving purpose to get trained early and well, and would also demonstrate our commitment to hands-on involvement in CQI. Second, if we tried to begin teams immediately at every entity, we wouldn't be able to monitor initial progress and discover what worked and what didn't.

We had decided to begin phase I at five health care facilities as well as the corporate office. The five facilities were St. Marys Hospital Medical Center in Madison, Wisconsin; St. Mary's Hospital at Blue Springs, Missouri (now part of another system as the result of an exchange of facilities); Cardinal Glennon Children's Hospital of St. Louis, Missouri; Good Samaritan Regional Health Center in Mt. Vernon, Illinois; and St. Francis Hospital in Maryville, Missouri.

These five hospitals offered a mix of entities, and their respective leaders believed they could support the effort that would be needed. We thought it was important to involve the corporate office right away so that the system management team would gain first-hand experience working on a quality improvement team.

Even though we were starting CQI with just six entities, Sister Mary Jean made it crystal clear that CQI was not an experiment. We had taken to heart the first principle of W. Edwards Deming's 14 points for management, which states, "Create constancy of purpose toward improvement of product and service."[1]

We didn't want anyone operating under the impression that we might jettison the plan if the first entities experienced difficulty. On the contrary, we expected to learn from the mistakes, missteps, and successes of the early teams. We would integrate the plan-do-check-act (PDCA) process (also called the Shewhart cycle after Walter Shewhart, the quality theorist who conceived it) not only into our work on quality improvement projects, but also into the systemwide implementation itself.

Before any entities could begin forming project teams, however, individuals had to be mentally prepared and structures in the facilities had to be organized for CQI. This preparation in our entities took the form of readiness screens.

## PURPOSE OF THE READINESS SCREENS

The readiness screens were checklists that entity steering teams had to complete, in sequence, before implementing the CQI curriculum or quality improvement teams. We viewed the screens as insurance against the false starts we had been warned about by other institutions. Readiness screens would

- Help each entity "break the ice" with CQI.

- Establish a consistent approach to the development and implementation of the CQI process.

- Give entity steering teams an opportunity to learn how CQI works in real work situations.

- Permit the entity steering teams to lead by example.

We originally expected every entity to complete the readiness screens by December 31, 1991. In fact, the first entity to complete them was St. Marys Hospital Medical Center in Madison, in March 1991. All the entities completed the screens by December 1992.

## THE CQI CURRICULUM

With assistance from Paul Plsek, we virtually created our own CQI curriculum. All that we had to start with were examples of courses designed for manufacturing industries. We used some of those curricula to give us a framework and then adapted the courses to the health care environment.

We wanted to provide a solid grounding in the concepts of quality, teamwork, process variation, and the tools of measurement and analysis. The courses—ranging in length from three hours to five days—would be offered in cycles, with participation determined by who was next to be on a team. As entities began creating their teams throughout phase I, those employees and physicians would be scheduled in the necessary courses.

Some people at one of the entities were upset when we turned down their request to be allowed to develop their own curriculum. We quickly reminded them that CQI was a systemwide effort, not a series of options for individual facilities to choose from as they wanted. It was challenging enough bringing instructors up to speed to teach one set of courses. We did not even want to imagine the confusion that would have erupted if 16 different curricula were being offered in an attempt to educate people in one quality management paradigm!

## THE PILOT PROJECTS

Pilot projects, required in the sixth screen, were the first opportunity the entity steering teams would have to practice working together on a project, collecting and analyzing data, and following the CQI model. We used the term *pilot project* with caution, making sure everyone knew that our commitment to CQI wasn't riding on a project's success or failure. All of the projects were to be small in scope, involving a work routine in which team members were directly involved.

It would be fair to say that, across the board, teams found their first efforts to be painstaking and laborious. Working through the unfamiliar steps of a team method to accomplish a relatively small project could be compared to a right-handed person trying to do all of their routine tasks left-handed.

Moreover, we were not creating CQI structures and practices in a clear field. All of our facilities, from corporate office to hospitals, already had well entrenched sets of systems, procedures, habits, customs, and routines. None of the CQI structures was a match for our current ways of operating in terms of strength, familiarity, or comfortableness.

Although we could admit to the mental models that were shaping our actions and opinions, that didn't lessen their grip on the system management team members as we crawled through the infant stages of CQI.

We were confident that we would follow the CQI team model because it was the "right" thing to do, but we were still operating inside of a paradigm in which teamwork seemed slow and cumbersome. Our life experience had been that we *really* could work faster and more effectively on our own turf and in our own way.

At the same time, though, we couldn't help but see the inefficiency of our individualistic styles. In an environment where each person focuses on his or her piece of the effort, responsibility for the outcome tends to be placed on the person who touched it last. The cumulative effects of the total process could easily go unseen. Thus, in the familiar paradigm, if something went wrong, the tendency was to lay the blame on a person instead of a process.

## TWO EXAMPLES THAT ILLUSTRATE THE POINT

Philip Crosby, one of the best known quality theorists in the United States, has said that "hassle elimination" (getting rid of the barriers that keep the job from getting done) and "quality improvement" are the same.[2] Sometimes we can see this most clearly with the little things.

One hassle we wanted to eliminate in the corporate office was the irregular and lengthy routing of mail among the system management team. We chose this as our team's first CQI project, and it was intentionally small in scope—like all the initial projects selected—so that we could focus on mastering the CQI process analysis tools. Our mission was to improve the cycle time for routing materials among the team. We developed a flowchart of what we thought the process was like.

When we posted the flowchart on a storyboard and asked for input, we received about 14 separate comments pointing out errors in the chart. Our team effort was a pure demonstration of people trying to improve a process without even knowing how the process worked! We had ignored one of the tenets of establishing a team, that is, having people who perform the process be part of it. None of our support staff was represented.

This project has entered the archives as a corporate legend because it was one of the longest, if not the longest, projects undertaken in the entire system. It took us 18 months to go from step one to step seven in our CQI problem-solving model! On the plus side, though, we get to use this project for learning purposes as a good example of a "bad example" of how to chart a process.

Our blindness to our own mail routing process had left us totally ineffective in eliminating a hassle. Before CQI, all we could do about it was wonder and complain and mentally blame somebody else for the inefficiency.

A second example has to do with the pull of the old paradigm to take things into our own hands, even when there's a workable process in place. One of the vice presidents had set up a process with her secretary for making detailed travel arrangements that specified her preferences for seat assignments, rental cars, and hotel accommodations.

During a trip early in the implementation, the vice president was unhappy to find that she did not get her preferred seat assignment on the plane. She assumed the secretary had dropped the ball and was prepared to take her to task. Then, she realized that the mistake had occurred not because the secretary didn't follow the process, but because she herself had interfered by calling the travel agent on her own and changing some of her arrangements. Minor though it was, the incident was a perfect example of how quality, as hassle elimination, is negatively affected when a special cause variation interferes with a process.

## AFTER THE READINESS SCREENS

As soon as an entity completed all eight screens, the steering committee's next job was to appoint the first three quality improvement teams and team leaders.

With these teams identified, the CQI awareness course, SSMHCS CQI: 100, could begin. Besides the team members, the classes included their respective managers, team leaders, facilitators, quality assurance staff, and employees who had been participants at the 1990 hands-on healers gathering. All team members were provided with the mission statement for their project, and the work of the team began.

Generally, teams, with a facilitator and a team leader, were to meet on a recommended schedule of once a week for one hour. Health care facilities always have diversely trained people working together, but working as equals on interdepartmental teams certainly was not a common practice in our system before CQI. We needed facilitators to be able to deal with the dynamics that occur when people at different places in the pecking order attempt to work as teammates.

Our legendary QIT also had a breakdown in this area because it was difficult at first for our facilitator to get used to telling system management it was doing something incorrectly. We were a while into our project before the facilitator was comfortable telling us when we went off the track.

In keeping with the idea that everyone on a QIT is equal, regardless of background or title, the team leaders aren't necessarily the ranking members. Leaders are selected based on the personal characteristics and abilities that fit the profile, rather than their position. For the early leaders, we recommended that individuals who had attended our January 1990 hands-on healers gathering be selected because they had at least some knowledge of CQI and had already demonstrated enthusiasm and leadership.

Both facilitators and leaders receive special training in the specific knowledge and skills needed to fulfill the role.

## EDUCATING TEAMS

In putting together our implementation plan and curriculum, we didn't want to limit ourselves to one quality theorist's ideas. Deming, however, with his emphasis on statistical process control and continuous education for everyone, provided the best basis for the solid foundation we wanted.

Providing system employees with an understanding of processes, variation, statistics, and customers would be essential for the teams' success.

## Process

All work is part of a process. This CQI principle is easy to remember as a statement, but it takes practice to begin seeing one's own work as a series of processes.

Analyzing the complex processes of patient care or hospital administration seems especially difficult because most people in health care are highly action-oriented, going from start to finish as quickly as possible without studying all the steps we are taking (or retaking) to get something done.

A goal of the curriculum was to have system personnel recognize that the process itself is the raw material of quality. And no amount of speed, experience, credentials, or good intentions can remedy a flawed process. We emphasized that quality improvement could only come about by analyzing the process, discovering the most significant problems in the process (usually pointing to unnecessary complexity or rework), and then designing or redesigning the process.

Our course instructors needed to get across that even though CQI training and team meetings would take time, poor processes were eating up a lot more time and had been doing so for a long while.

To the supervisor untrained in CQI, for example, it may not make much difference if a nurse is away from patients because she is dealing with a recurring problem on the unit or because she is participating in a QIT meeting. But there is huge difference. In the first case, her time is repetitively wasted, and in the second, her time is invested in an activity that will improve the quality of care patients receive.

It is a turning point in CQI when specific processes, rather than just an unending flow of work, begin to be discernible for people. A few months into phase I, someone who worked on an early team commented to us, "Now I'm seeing processes everywhere I look!" That seemed to be a common experience. Even employees who weren't working on teams themselves, but were around people who were, began to see the processes of their jobs.

In phase I, through system management's communication and example, we intended that managers in the entities not only see their own work as a series of processes, but also take responsibility for the larger systems on which their employees' processes depend.

## Variation

In chapter 1, we wrote of Deming's red bead experiment and how it had brought home to us the principle of variation in processes. Although normal variation is present in every process, the more and greater the variations in a repetitive process, the poorer the quality of the outcome. A key lesson for teams was learning to analyze a process for variation and plot it on a control chart, which displays the upper and lower limits of variation in a process. The plotted marks give a graphic picture of just where the variation in a process goes beyond the normal limits (see Figure 2.1).

By understanding the difference between common cause variations (those that occur within the limits) and special cause variations (those that one would suspect whenever a result fell outside of the control limits), teams are first able to focus on bringing a process into control and then continuously fine-tuning the process to reduce the amount of variation in a process (see Figures 2.2 and 2.3).

When a team is able to distinguish between common cause and special cause variations, it can avoid two errors of process improvement. A type I error is taking a corrective action in a process when

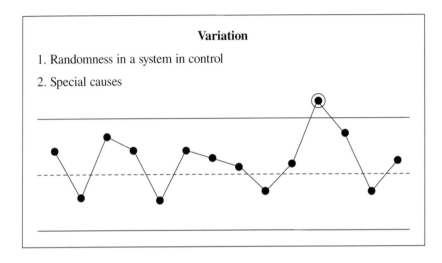

**Figure 2.1.** Variation displayed in a control chart.

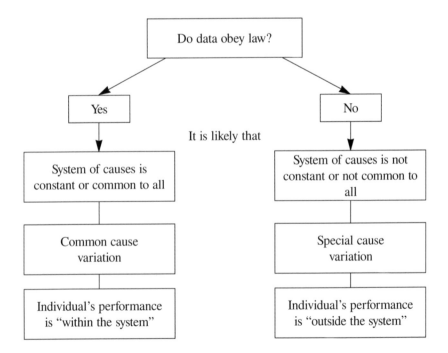

**Figure 2.2.** Interpreting variation.

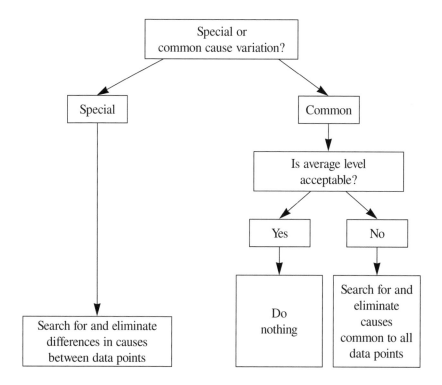

**Figure 2.3.** Acting on variation.

none is really needed. This is sometimes referred to as "tinkering." A type II error is failing to act when action is needed.

We have included an example of a control chart from one of our entity teams, showing the variation in discharge waiting times before and after the team's improvement project (see Figure 2.4).

## Statistics

Our education process had to include basic training in the statistics that comprise the objective data of quality management. While certain employees were comfortable with the use of statistics, others were concerned about having to learn to deal with numbers.

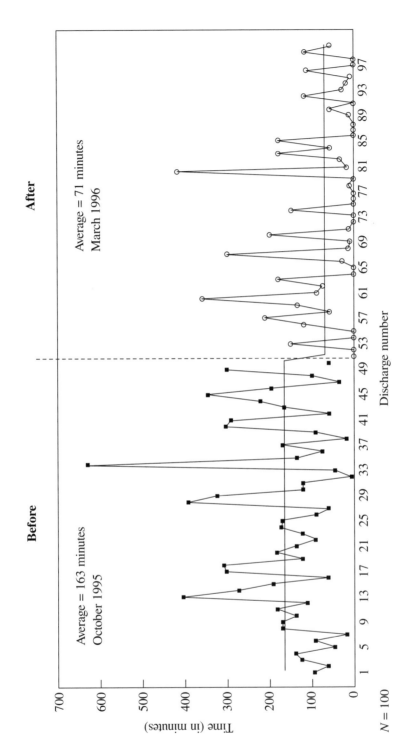

**Figure 2.4.** Before and after control chart: Discharge waiting time (in minutes).

As Paul Plsek had assured us, the statistics needed for CQI aren't high-level math. The numbers are usually plotted on a chart or graph to give a visual display to the objective measurement of some process. Without the quantifiable evidence—minutes, hours, steps, people, telephone rings, spills, pills, pieces of paper, billing errors, lab errors, hand-offs, trips to central supply, and so on—all we have are anecdotes, perceptions, opinions, generalizations, hunches, and suspicions.

Learning to understand variation and to bring a process into statistical control required a use of numbers that not many of us were used to. Yet just as manufacturing industries had come to see years earlier, we now knew that without numerical measurement we had no way to accurately assess the extent of our entities' waste and rework—the dual culprits of poor quality.

## Customers and Suppliers

People in the SSM Health Care System also had to gain an understanding of what was meant by *customer*, a word not only not commonly used in health care, but also considered by some to have a negative connotation.

After an early CQI presentation by Sister Mary Jean, a physician made an impassioned plea that we not call patients "customers." He went on for about five minutes as to why the term would be the ruination of health care. This reaction, we suspect, was typical of many veteran caregivers who are reluctant to give up a notion from the traditional paradigm of health care.

The word *patient* has taken on a certain aura because, in theory, it refers to someone who is respectfully cared for and tended to. In reality, the experience of many patients (including both of us) in doctors' waiting rooms, hospital emergency rooms, admissions areas, diagnostic areas, surgical holding areas, and nursing floors is that "patient" is exactly what they have to be!

Yet we believe that traditionalists are attached to the term *patient* because it connotes someone who is passive. The idea that people would be active participants in their own care is not something highly desired by some practitioners.

In an untransformed culture, there is a certain logic to the care-givers' preference for people who are willing to wait patiently, uncomplainingly, and unassertively—in a sort of childlike, depen-dent manner. This way, the professionals can go about their business uninterrupted by the "uninformed" concerns of their patients.

When a health care institution begins pursuing quality manage-ment and adhering to the principles of continuous improvement, however, the idea of an independent and informed "customer," rather than a patient "patient," must enter the picture. The creation of partnerships between customers and suppliers is a critical princi-ple of quality management.

To system management, replacing "patient" with "customer" seemed, at first, justified and appropriate. We thought it would dra-matically convey the paradigm shift that we intended to cause in our relationship to the people we served.

But early in the implementation process, we realized that trying to convince everyone in our system of the wisdom of this new term would not be the best use of our time. We compromised by using the phrase *patients and other customers*. We did not want to forget that we are engaged in a customer-supplier relationship, yet we did not have to demand that people always use the term *customer*. If it made it easier for physicians and nurses to continue calling people patients while they started treating them like customers, that would be a compromise we could live with.

By using the phrase *patients and other customers,* we remind ourselves that patients are indeed customers, and we also remind ourselves of all of the other customers who spend their time in our facilities.

A customer is anyone on the receiving end of one of our processes. Physicians, nurses, technicians and other professionals, employees, vendors, and visitors are all customers at some point along the way. The supplier is whoever is putting the effort, information, or materials into the process to produce an output.

## THE WORK OF THE TEAM

Part of the team training in quality management is learning to shift the ingredients of decision making from opinions and intuition to objective facts gathered by analysis. The analytical tools of CQI are flowcharts, cause-and-effect diagrams, Pareto charts, run charts, histograms, and scatter diagrams, in addition to the control charts previously mentioned. Some of these tools are taught by the facilitator as part of just-in-time training. We've included a series of examples of these types of analysis tools from some of our own entities' quality improvement teams (see Figures 2.5 to 2.11).

As the team identifies a project to work on, it establishes a measurable goal and begins to work toward that goal, collecting data, testing a possible solution on a small scale, and monitoring progress.

Members know whether or not their work of correcting or improving a process or designing a new process has been successful because they can measure the specific progress they have made toward the goal. The results, positive or negative, are studied to see what has been learned. The next action may be to start the process again or to incorporate the solution into the way of working, document and communicate it, and, perhaps replicate it in other departments or entities. This is the process of planning improvements referred to earlier as PDCA.

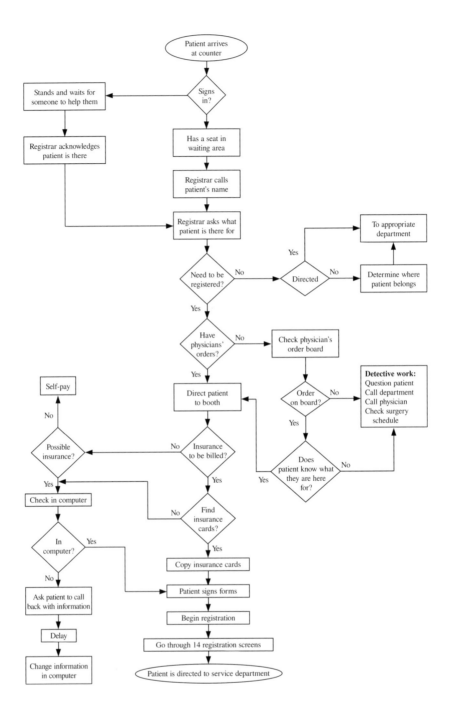

**Figure 2.5.** Flowchart of current outpatient registration process from patient's point of view.

50

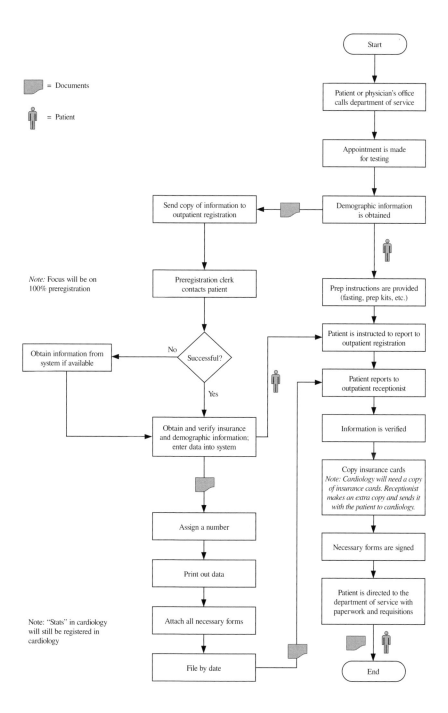

**Figure 2.6.** Flowchart of proposed process: High-level flowchart for proposed outpatient preregistration process.

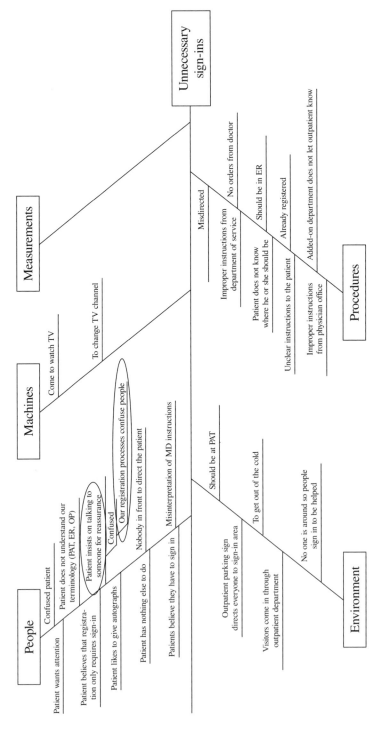

**Figure 2.7.** Cause-and-effect diagram. Cause-and-effect diagrams are tools that illuminate the sources (cause) of both desirable and undesirable results or conditions (effect).

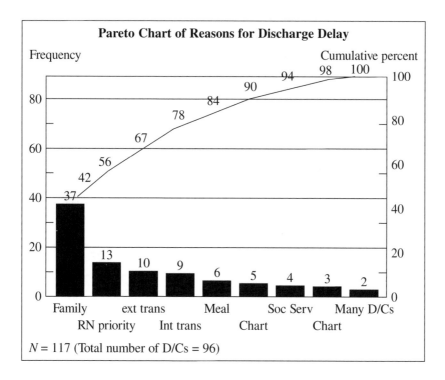

**Figure 2.8.** Pareto analysis. Pareto charts illustrate the frequency with which actual problems occur. These charts are helpful in prioritizing the order in which problems should be addressed by a team.

## THE CQI MODEL

Unlike manufacturing industries with their assembly line processes, hospitals rarely have had articulated, documented processes for every activity. Often, the way a job is carried out in a hospital is based on the strengths, preferences, habits, or routines of the individual doing it. Changes can occur depending on the shift, day of the week, or time of day. When a task is passed on to another, it is more in the mode of an oral history than a by-the-book instruction. The new person who takes over the job then makes his or her own changes, until there is so much variation that there is no process!

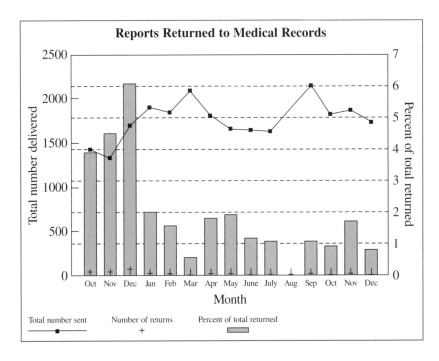

**Figure 2.9.** Run chart. Run charts are prepared to graphically reflect data collected over a period of time for the purpose of noting trends.

It might seem surprising that we as health care professionals have had such a personalized approach to our jobs. Yet inside of a paradigm that emphasizes an individual's performance rather than processes within a system, such ad hoc work isn't surprising at all. Mostly we have counted on individual competence, goodwill, and professional pride to see us through. If things broke down, we always had the bad apple theory.

When we committed the system to continuous quality improvement, we adopted a method for analyzing and improving processes that we call the SSM Health Care System seven-step CQI model (see Figure 2.12). The model brings together two approaches for teams to use in designing process improvements. One was Florida

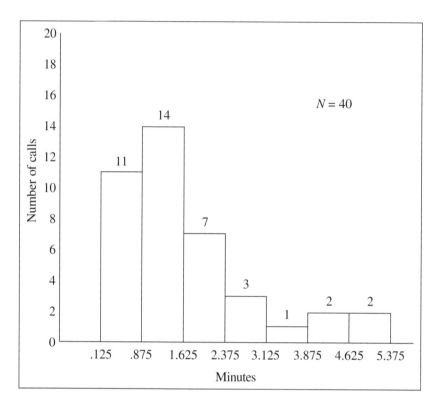

**Figure 2.10.** Histogram of call light response time. Histograms measure the frequency of an occurrence over a period of time. The left axis pertains to frequency and the right axis pertains to the variable being tracked.

Power and Light's seven-step storyboard, and the other was Paul Plsek's design/redesign process approach. The SSM Health Care System was the first to integrate these two approaches to create a problem-solving/process design model for a systemwide implementation of CQI.

We adopted the two-pronged model to give our entities the flexibility to completely design processes that previously had not existed or were only loosely defined. The approach was to start with the customer needs and then design processes that meet those needs.

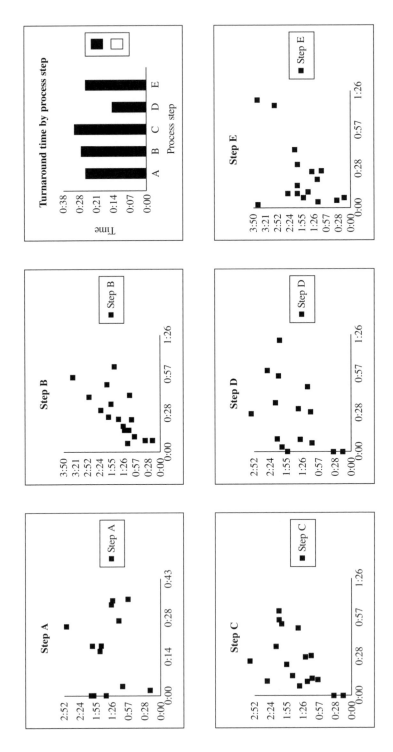

**Figure 2.11.** Scatter diagram analysis of medication turnaround time. Scatter diagrams allow a team to chart the relationship between variables so that possible correlations or patterns can be detected.

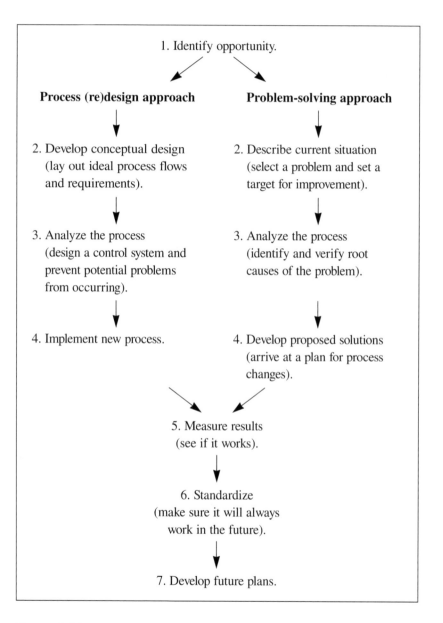

**Figure 2.12.** SSM Health Care System seven-step CQI model.

In addition to the existing work that required process design, we also were doing many new things in our entities: creating new services, setting up new programs, and installing new equipment. We previously had not had a disciplined way to answer the question, "How do we want to design the process to get this done?"

With the model, team members beginning to work on a project would first identify the opportunity of the project. That is, they would ask, "How can this process better fulfill the customer's expectations?" and "What are the outcomes we wish to achieve?" Those questions would ideally stimulate a whole new orientation, different from "This is what I'm used to," "This is how I've always done it, " or "I like to do it this way." The team would have the freedom to start at ground zero, if necessary, and engage in thinking together about how to design or redesign a process, looking backward from a satisfied customer's perspective.

Our CQI model provides two entry points to QIT projects. When a process is relatively well defined, the problem-solving approach is used. And when there is no clear process, or the process is unworkable, the process (re)design approach is used.

This model allows teams to articulate the goals, activities, and outcomes of the project. It also provides a way to communicate what is being studied, what the changes are, and how the changes are standardized and incorporated with the flow of work.

* * *

*To this point, we have provided an overview of why and how we undertook continuous quality improvement across the SSM Health Care System in 1990. In the next few chapters, we relate some of what we have learned and accomplished in the past seven years of our CQI implementation.*

## Notes

1. W. Edwards Deming, *Out of the Crisis* (Cambridge, Mass.: MIT Center for Advanced Engineering Study, 1986).

2. Philip B. Crosby, *Quality Without Tears* (New York: New American Library, 1984).

3

# A SAMPLER
# OF CRITICAL
# ISSUES WITH
# NO SIMPLE
# ANSWERS

*In this chapter, we share our experiences with a variety of the issues that continuous improvement has pushed to the surface. We do not view any of these critical issues as resolved. We suspect that they will remain ever-present questions on a journey that's always in progress—provoking our thinking and prompting ongoing dialog.*

Once it was put into motion, continuous quality improvement splashed over everything in the SSM Health Care System. Some issues—like teamwork—came to the forefront by design, while others—like job security—would have arisen in the 1990s no matter what management structures were in place.

## WHY DO WE NEED CQI?

One question we heard from some people in the system was, "Why do we even need CQI?" In early 1990, the system was doing exceedingly well. Our hospitals' reputations were good. We had achieved a fourfold increase in net income between 1988 and 1989, even as we increased our charity care by 30 percent.

Our response, and the message we continue to convey passionately, is, "No matter how well we are doing, continuous quality improvement means there is always a way to do everything better." The question we would ask was, "If we've been able to do so well without clearly designed processes, what could we accomplish if we had such processes in place everywhere?"

Our motivation for continuous improvement was not based on our performance, but on our mission and values. If we were being true to our mission, the question to ask was not "Why CQI?," but rather, "How are we enhancing quality?"

From the founding of the system in 1986, Sister Mary Jean had emphasized that the SSM Health Care System's strength demanded leadership, not satisfaction with the status quo. This is a potentially sensitive message for employees to hear. We have to acknowledge their efforts, while still talking straight about the many areas in need of change and improvement. We cannot afford to be complacent simply because we are doing better than others.

In her closing talk at the 1990 conference, Sister Mary Jean gave a verbal "tour" of a future world where CQI was firmly in place (see Figure 3.1). We wanted this to serve as a reminder that improvement is always a process, never a destination.

Here, in the SSM Health Care System, all of us work with the conviction that whatever we're doing can always and must always be improved.

We look to the design of a process or the absence of a process to discover why and where the defects exist.

Everyone who works here is seen as a compassionate and intelligent individual who has energy, ideas, and a desire to serve others.

We ensure quality in everything by continually analyzing and improving our processes.

Those who are familiar with a specific process are the ones who collect the data and apply their CQI tools to correct what isn't working.

We solve problems and improve processes without regard for traditional, artificial departmental boundaries.

Our customers and our suppliers are our partners, establishing long-term relationships with us because they have a stake in the quality of the care and service we provide.

In our relationships with coworkers we support each other in doing excellent work all of the time.

**Figure 3.1.** CQI future vision statement.

We also developed a number of themes that we return to again and again, in systemwide communications and within each entity.

- Change is the one thing we can count on. Health care professionals—clinical and administrative—must be prepared for continuous personal and institutional change.

- Many of the ways of providing care that worked in the past have to be surrendered—not necessarily because they didn't work then, but because they don't work now.

- A willingness to learn is central to improved quality.

In the years before CQI, Sister Mary Jean had noticed and spoken about the shifting attitudes toward health care. More and more

Americans have become unwilling to settle for passive or unquestioning care. They want to be responsible and knowledgeable about their health. They are moving from the traditional care of medication, technology, and a belief in "doctor knows best" to alternative forms of treatment with more attention on education, prevention, nutrition, and fitness. They are looking for partners, not parents.

## WORKING WITH WHAT WE HAVE

Our system, in 1990, was operating 21 health care facilities and six health businesses in five states, with 13,500 employees. We felt safe in assuming that all of us together—administrators, employees, and physicians—fairly represented the attitudes, abilities, personalities, and backgrounds that one would find throughout American health care.

We were not dealing with a homogeneous group that would uniformly welcome this effort and carry it out in exactly the same way or succeed to the same degree. We had to give latitude to a range of reactions and opinions. We expected that some of our entities would embrace CQI wholeheartedly, some would be reasonably accepting of it, and some would be lukewarm. Judging from the experience in the past seven-plus years, our early expectation proved correct.

Since this was a systemwide effort, participation by the entities would be required. One part of our own preparation for leading this large effort was to more or less brace ourselves to hear whatever reactions were evoked. Although we could mandate implementation of the CQI structure, we could not control attitudes or opinions. We could not order people to love CQI or to be enthusiastic about it.

In any organization, people choose which aspects of their work they will be deeply engaged in and which they will deal with more superficially. Some employees enjoy opportunities to network among different departments and some like to stay on their own turf. Some love long-term projects and others prefer to focus on immediate concerns. Some always take on volunteer or "extracurricular" activities and some seldom do. Similarly, employees at every level—from professional to unskilled—span the gamut between skeptical and open, resistant to change and eager to change, apathetic and enthusiastic.

All that we as system leaders could ask was that, no matter what their level of responsibility, people take on the tasks that have to be accomplished in their departments regarding CQI, just as they are expected to take on any other part of their job. To make our expectations as clear as possible, we listed in the CQI manual the operational roles of management, employees, and physicians as they pertain to CQI (see the appendix).

Our conviction was that as CQI's principles and tools were infused throughout facilities, there would be a critical mass of physicians, managers, nurses, and other staff members who would be won over by the possibilities of continuous quality improvement, even when faced with the risks and challenges such a massive change presented.

A quote that Sister Mary Jean had found to be reassuring in this regard was from Marilyn Ferguson, in her book *The Aquarian Conspiracy*. Ferguson wrote,

> *If we are to find our way across troubled waters, we are better served by the company of those who have built bridges, who have moved beyond despair and inertia . . . they know that opportunity appears in many guises, that dissolution and pain are necessary stages in renewal and that 'failures' can be powerfully instructive. Aware that change can only come from within, they are gentle in their confrontation.*[1]

Establishing the foundation for a long-term transformation in each entity would fall to the leaders who were on site every day. Our job was to inform, persuade, convince, and enroll enough of those leaders so that CQI would have a core of champions at every site.

## CHANGE VS. INERTIA

What really does compel people to take on something new? We fear sometimes that the traditional culture of employees simply doing what they were told in a hierarchical environment trained them to put their brains in neutral when they came to work.

As we have found in spending time with employees, it certainly isn't that they are not bright and committed people. It is more likely that when they come to work, they put on the institutional culture like a jacket until it's time to take it off at the end of the day.

Truly, this condition is one of our biggest disappointments in implementing CQI. Is there any way that people will get excited about improving something that could work much better? How can we help people unleash the creativity that exists within them? Is everything really so great just as it is?

Someone sent an e-mail note to Sister Mary Jean saying, "I understand your desires about this creativity thing, but we don't have time to meet." That kind of thinking puts a limit on the possibility of being creative. There seems to be a belief that creativity has to come in large doses and can only be pursued by people when they aren't "at work." So they say, "We'd love to solve that problem, but there's no time!"

We wonder, do we need a *lot* of time to ask ourselves, "Is there a better way to do this?"

## TIME

The concern about time—the time that CQI implementation takes—has been universal. And we have faced it head on.

Yes, we do ask busy people to take hours out of their "regular" jobs to go to classes, to meet with their teams, and to do data gathering and analysis.

For some employees serving on teams, this becomes an issue of guilt. They have to leave their posts without a replacement to go to a class or a team meeting.

For some supervisors, having employees be away from their assignment poses scheduling problems and adds more work to others' schedules. Yet manufacturing companies, utilities, and health care facilities have been able to work out these problems.

None of us in system management tries to pretend that the time barrier doesn't exist or that we have a simple solution for it. We ask people to deal with it professionally, arranging their schedules for the least amount of interruption or inconvenience of coworkers.

Once, when a physician at one of the St. Louis hospitals approached Sister Mary Jean during a site visit and asked her how she was planning to provide coverage for those who were in CQI classes and meetings, she simply said, "I'm not planning to do anything." The physician walked away unhappy.

Although the response may have seemed terse, it exemplifies both our stand and our commitment. In a culture of quality, people are assumed to have the intelligence, dedication, and goodwill to get their jobs done. While the tendency is to see CQI as an "extra" job, it is not. Training for and implementing CQI, in accord with our system's mission, isn't an add-on to the "real" work that people are supposed to be doing.

We realized that the degree to which those of us in system management began to apologize for the "inconvenience" of CQI would be the degree to which we would be reinforcing the idea that continuous improvement was an option, an add-on, or another passing fad. Transforming the culture includes trusting people to solve problems creatively—including problems with time.

## TEAMS AND TEAMWORK

At the system management level we have put a lot of personal energy into developing ourselves as members of a team. For each of us at varying times, the pressures of planning and decision making have sometimes led us to wonder about the immediate value of spending time on team development processes.

The view might easily have been that if we have gotten this far on our talents, leadership skills, and experience, why take time now to become good team members? This is probably a question every corporate leadership group raises—especially in moments of unwelcome "feedback," or evaluation.

What we can see, after several years, is that the work we have done together to discover our mental models, our work and leadership styles, and our ways of learning and communicating really does pay off. We haven't changed one another, nor do we expect to. But we have a clarity and a greater degree of patience in thrashing things out together because we understand our differences.

As a team we have come to appreciate our diversity because we've taken the time to distinguish it for what it is. A couple of us are great at listening and clarifying the points others make. Some of us like saying all of our ideas out loud until we find the one we will really go to bat for. Others want to think things through first and then say what we believe. Some of us interrupt and get impatient. Some of us are thin-skinned. Some of us are great at giving positive feedback to our teammates, but are stingy with constructive criticism.

Some of us put everything on the table, and some of us quietly gather support for our views before or after meetings.

In other words, the system management team members are as random a collection of personalities as one would find anywhere. The breakthrough for us as a team is that we have recognized we cannot let our temperaments, styles, likes, and dislikes interfere with our working together. Within a CQI culture, the work of the team really supersedes the work of the individual in many leadership activities.

In the not-too-distant past, not everyone on the system management team would have felt comfortable having a peer relationship with the president and CEO, especially one who was also a religious sister. The work we've done to develop a team has empowered people to be free to offer Sister Mary Jean suggestions and ideas more openly.

We question, though, whether this openness exists in the rest of the organization. Do the line employees feel comfortable going to their managers and suggesting alternatives? Do the managers feel comfortable going to department heads? Do department heads go to the vice president?

From this perspective, when we look at leadership teams that work or don't work in our system, we would say that it is the commitment to operating as a diverse team that makes the difference. Rather than wishing everyone were alike so there would be no disagreement or conflict, we now actually recognize that real value is lost if one of us not there, because we are missing his or her viewpoint and approach.

This is no different than if a team in a hospital is creating a center of excellence, for example in cardiology. The team would gather a cardiologist, a cardiovascular surgeon, a nurse, a pharmacist, and so on. Everybody brings something different and valuable, and the group is not whole without each one of them.

Some of the administrative councils—as well as other department teams—in the various facilities do not have this appreciation for the strength of differences. They do not really work together, and it is noticeable in the results they produce.

In the St. Louis Health Care Network management team, which we will say more about later, three of the presidents really enjoy working as team members. Part of their job is to keep influencing the other leaders in the direction of genuine teamwork. This isn't easy among talented and busy people who always have somewhere else to go. They virtually have a miniculture to transform from the Lone Ranger model to the team model.

In each of our departments in the facilities and in the corporate office, similar movement toward teams must occur. It begins with recognizing the gravitational pull toward the status quo.

With each of the quality improvement teams, the principles of teamwork apply as well. The teams have to be put together with an eye on what human resources, knowledge, and experience are needed on the project. Once that kind of team is assembled, it only makes sense to value the input of all participants because of the perspective they bring.

A switchboard operator at one of our hospitals said she was amazed at her experience of being on a team. She first had to get used to the idea that she was chosen to be on a team, then she was surprised that her teammates listened to what she had to say and accepted her input. Knowing that she had influence in her job gave her a different attitude toward everything.

## CYNICISM

Some employees and managers bring a cynical attitude to the CQI effort. We publicly acknowledged that it is common, especially in service professions, for people to try to disguise their cynicism as simply maturity or realism, practicality or reasonableness.

Knowing that among our thousands of employees there would be cynical views about CQI, we could only accept the fact that such attitudes are usually protection against being conned or disappointed.

To deal with cynicism, we continue to be careful never to present CQI as a panacea for the things that don't work in our entities. Nor do we say that the SSM Health Care System will become Utopia.

Like most institutions, we have had our share of projects, campaigns, and programs that began with a flourish and then faded away. We have had executives, managers, and supervisors who have promised things and then not delivered. Still, we are unwilling to let the bite of cynicism stop us from taking on large commitments.

## PHYSICIANS IN CQI

We took the case for physician participation in CQI directly to more than 50 leading practitioners on the staffs of SSM Health Care System facilities. At a meeting in Phoenix, Arizona, in October 1990, Sister Mary Jean appealed for a partnership based on mutual concern about the state of health care delivery and a mutual commitment to quality.

It was our belief that physicians who were willing to participate on quality improvement teams with a cross-section of hospital employees would take on a whole new way of exercising leadership in health care.

Through more than seven years of CQI, physician participation has not grown in the way we had hoped or anticipated.

Of all the people in a hospital, physicians should be the most apt to see the value of continuous improvement and its methods. Physicians' use of the scientific method for diagnosis and treatment matches the CQI discipline of using objective data rather than opinions for decision making. Their training predisposes them to the process of continuous improvement.

For a short time we had entertained the idea of providing a separate, shorter curriculum for our entities' staff physicians in order to make the courses more amenable to their schedules. But ultimately we decided that physicians would be included in the same educational curriculum as everyone else. We were reluctant to perpetuate separations among clinical care providers.

Some physicians have taken very favorably to CQI and have participated in classes and on teams. Where they do, they are champions of CQI and are willing to encourage other physicians to participate.

One stumbling block for major physician involvement has been, not surprisingly, schedule conflicts with classes or team meetings. Another barrier we hear of is that teams, of necessity, use a much smaller database in their analyses of processes than meets scientific requirements. Some physicians may balk at the data.

Until the physicians become partners on the patient care team, and do not have to lead it, we will not make the progress we are committed to making in improving the quality of our clinical care. Without the necessary education in CQI and the experience of working on teams as equals, physicians will continue to approach their role as the leader, even if they are not the best prepared to provide leadership.

Cause for encouragement, however, is that more doctors are organized in large group practices today. In 1991, the system hospitals just in St. Louis employed only about 20 or 30 physicians. In 1997, there were more than 500 employed physicians. When they were only organized around a medical staff, there was not much pressure for physicians to improve their methods. Now at conferences we hear physicians saying they need more data to better manage practice patterns and better manage care.

We now are on the cusp of a major shift that will have doctors wanting to be more involved in improving the quality of care, reducing costs, and reducing length of stay. They know that to be successful, they have to be in a managed care program. And managed care contracts require more than lowered costs; they require high quality. They cannot just do what they did in the past.

The challenge is to provide physicians not only the data, but also enroll them in learning how to use the tools to analyze the data and review the processes so that they can make the appropriate changes.

Given the external pressures, we now see—after seven years of slow movement with physicians—a much greater opportunity to communicate the principles of CQI and have them become stronger champions of it.

## REPLICATING BEST PRACTICES

One of the primary goals of implementing CQI systemwide was to have good ideas replicated across our facilities. We established a Quality Resource Center to serve as a clearinghouse for data and for storyboards on quality projects so that solutions could be spread around. The corporate communications department also created the *Quality Chronicle* to share news about successes.

To our disappointment, replication is only slowly beginning to catch on. We think that part of the lag is the independent nature of the entities. In our culture, being able to operate on one's own is so treasured that taking on another facility's idea seems like a violation of autonomy.

We suspect that there may actually be managers and supervisors who say to themselves, "If one of my bosses finds out that I called so-and-so to find out how to do something, what are they going to think?"

We also find a sense of territorial uniqueness, as in, "Our situation [or my situation] is just so different here. That wouldn't work."

This is demonstrated in an example provided by one of our long-time entity managers who became president of an acquired hospital. She was rather surprised to find out that even though the hospital had been in the system for more than a year, CQI had not yet been implemented. Employees at the hospital, hearing about CQI for months through system communications, eagerly asked the new president when they could begin working on it.

Personal concerns and apprehensions, territoriality, and the fear of having to give up familiar ways of operating that have always worked are part of all of us. As a still fairly young system, we have not yet imbedded the principle of contributing to one another as institutions.

Yet in individual instances we have seen how thrilled people are when someone from another hospital asks for information about a new process. To ask someone "How did you do that?" not only gains knowledge for the person asking, but it also reinforces the creative efforts of the individual or team that proposed the solution. It gives people real joy to be able to share their achievements with others in the system.

How to break through the complacency or superiority that keeps one facility from asking another for good ideas is a question that we repeatedly address.

One area where we are beginning to see some more exchanges of information is among entity presidents who are seeking out ideas at the strategic planning level. This is a start, but the transfer of knowledge needs to begin flowing more freely.

At our 1996 leadership conference, we set up what we called a showcase for sharing designs and redesigns from each facility as a means of recognizing good ideas and provoking replication. We are coming to believe that only by repeatedly asking for and displaying successful efforts will we as a system start taking advantage of the creative problem-solving resources available to us.

It is incongruous that a quality culture not be open to solutions, regardless of where they come from. The companies in other industries that are recognized for quality are ones that have constantly and unabashedly looked outside as well as inside to learn how to improve their operations. A major sign of our system's cultural transformation will occur when our entities are routinely sharing, learning from and replicating solutions among themselves.

We have made progress from the days before we were a system, when our large urban hospitals would never dream of replicating an idea from a smaller institution. But it has only been in the past year or so, within the structure set up by system management, that entity presidents have actively sought out the best practices of their colleagues.

In one example, St. Joseph Hospital of Kirkwood, looked to our 1996 Oklahoma State Quality Award–winning Bone & Joint Hospital for best practices. Two of the highest-rated strengths of the Oklahoma City hospital were its exceptional customer satisfaction levels and its strong human resource development and management.

It made eminent sense that St. Joseph would study its counterpart for practices to replicate in those areas. The Kirkwood hospital is taking steps to replicate Bone & Joint's customer feedback action plan, to improve response time for customer concerns and complaints. The hospital is also patterning an employee development design after the Oklahoma hospital's high-performance work system.

We are confident that as our entities reap the benefits of one another's ingenuity and creativity, by allowing themselves to "copy" from each other, the idea of replicating will take hold. Reluctance has just been another example of how difficult it is to move from the old paradigm to the new.

Benchmarking, or learning the best practices of other organizations, has not yet caught on in any significant way, either. This is not surprising, because it, too, requires a willingness to acknowledge that someone else is doing something better.

As with many issues in the system, it is taking time for us to change not only our ways of doing things, but also our way of *thinking* about things. Replication and benchmarking are two areas that require a way of thinking that is larger than the attachment to the individual's or local institution's ideas or accomplishments.

## EDUCATION

We invested much time and money in the development and implementation of the CQI curriculum. Thousands of employees and managers have gone through the classes and use what they've learned in their team projects.

Part of the sign of our commitment was system management members' taking four to six weeks to teach CQI courses in the first couple of years. People in the entities couldn't overlook the importance of CQI when they would see Bill Schoenhard, the chief operating officer, teaching courses six times a year.

A disappointment for some system management team members is that their opportunities to teach CQI courses have waned. Bill Thompson, at first, taught four to five weeks a year. But that time commitment wasn't sustainable. It became more appropriate to move the teaching responsibilities to middle management staff because they also work with the people they teach. By being able to instruct peers and employees in CQI tools, the middle managers not only are passing on knowledge, but also training themselves in being teachers, mentors, and facilitators instead of directors. Still, the opportunity to sharpen the edge of personal knowledge through the preparation of courses is missed by upper management.

One of the most satisfying developments in our CQI educational process is that some people have been able to find out how much they actually enjoy teaching. The opportunity for managers and many line employees who had no prior experience in front of a class to discover that teaching was something they could do well is exciting for us and for them. It has been a concrete demonstration of how CQI both develops and empowers people.

In opening up a new area of skill, some of the novice teachers were unknowingly preparing themselves to take on larger accountabilities. One example is a director of respiratory therapy who started teaching CQI courses. His confidence as a leader grew from that experience, and today he is an executive vice president and COO of one of our hospitals.

We attribute the success of CQI teachers not only to their increase in confidence and leadership, but also to the fact that in teaching the CQI principles and tools, and how to apply them, they incorporated them into their own work. The team leader training in particular, CQI 301, has opened a whole new outlet for talent that might not have been noticed. A person who may be stagnating in a job that's grown too easy or familiar is reinvigorated by the challenge of leading quality teams.

One of the biggest difficulties we faced in CQI education was the lack of time and ability to go back and improve the courses, based on all that we have learned. It takes a lot of time and resources to just maintain what we have. A related issue is, now that we have trained a thousand people, how do we go back and retrain them if we make fundamental changes?

Just in the past year, Barb Spreadbury—corporate director of the Quality Resource Center, the system's primary educator, and curriculum developer—has assembled a group of instructors to develop some guiding principles for updating CQI courses. They used class evaluations and postclass participant surveys and facilitator input to create the principles.

After seven years of use, the curriculum's purpose and structure remains valid and viable. The group, however, made several suggestions. Among those are suggestions to simplify the manual and teaching materials, recognize more diverse learning styles, recognize a diverse audience, have leadership groups in courses, and review the courses annually for timeliness.

To keep the level of the curriculum at a high quality, time has to be made for instructor teams to systematically go through all of the course manuals and begin improving and updating them.

## PASSING ON THE CULTURE

An issue intimately related to that of education is how to keep including and educating all of the new people that have come into our system through acquisitions.

We have added six new hospitals since CQI began. In most cases we kept the administrative staffs—who had not been trained in CQI—in the same place, or moved them to other system facilities. This presents the situation of having people in leadership positions, typically responsible for bringing the CQI culture to others, who did not even know what that culture is.

An example of this occurred when we promoted the president of a hospital we had acquired to the post of executive vice president, reporting to a new regional president. Neither of these executives had prior exposure to our culture before joining the system. Thus, no one at the top of this particular region was acculturated with the values and the philosophy that we are working to infuse by means of CQI.

These particular people are talented. And having new people coming in is good, because it keeps an organization vibrant and strong. But when new people become concentrated in a particular area, the ideal of cultural transformation loses its champions.

## THE QUESTION OF JOB SECURITY

People in our facilities sometimes refer to staff reductions within the system as a violation of our system's values. "If this is a quality organization that puts people first," they say, "how can we reconcile layoffs?"

We admit that this it is a painful situation to deal with, and we have not yet found a good way to do it. One thing we are sure of, though, is that sometimes reductions have to happen.

Many of the jobs that employees now feel they have a right to keep were created in an entirely different era of health care. Hospitals were gearing up for high inpatient volume and ever-increasing sophistication in tertiary care. We kept adding people, and now—when cost reduction has become a central focus—we still have them on the payroll.

Like all health care institutions, we are having to reduce our numbers. This is never an easy thing for executives to do. What makes it harder is confronting the attitude of entitlement among people who mistakenly got the idea that the SSM Health Care System owed them lifelong employment.

In a society where competitiveness and downsizing are no longer new concepts, it is disheartening to learn that some people in our system have not yet grasped that quality performance, not entitlement, protects job security.

•••••••••••••••••••••••••••••••••••••

*The issues and concerns that surface in a period of great organizational change are rarely resolved for good. Just as the environment we live and work in keeps changing, so do our viewpoints and approaches. We are resolved to not have the "final word" on any of these critical questions.*

## Note

1. Marilyn Ferguson, *The Aquarian Conspiracy* (New York: Jeremy Tarcher, 1980), 36–37.

# 4

# THE DEMAND FOR LEADERSHIP IN A QUALITY CULTURE

*Leadership in our system has been both gratifying in its unexpected presence and disappointing in its scarcity. In this chapter we look at examples of both conditions.*

••••••••••••••••••••••••••••••••

In an institution with as many entrenched cultures as the SSM Health Care System, major change was bound to be met with some resistance. We were prepared for it, and we were confident that we could work through it as a system if we had strong leadership.

Perhaps the most pervasive resistance to CQI comes from the uncomfortableness of change itself. All of us in system management could see how we grappled with change—in our work styles, in our resistance to teamwork, in our response to criticism. The important thing, we believed, was that no matter how difficult it got, we could not let ourselves be stopped because of our own or others' reluctance.

Early in CQI we acknowledged the common fear of change and expressed understanding for those who found it difficult. In listening to people express their concerns, however, we did not try to hide fact that change was going to happen. Right from the outset we said that if CQI is not something you can deal with, then it may be necessary for you to find someplace else to work. That might have seemed harsh, but we couldn't imagine circumstances in which CQI would present insurmountable obstacles for anyone who was truly committed to the system's mission and values. If someone did not accept CQI, it would not be that they couldn't, but simply that they wouldn't.

To try to balance the burden of change, we encouraged leadership, courage, and creativity. We promised that we in system management would push ourselves beyond where we were comfortable, and we asked other leaders to do the same. We appealed for authenticity in acknowledging that the old ways of interacting with patients, managing employees, and relating to coworkers were just no longer satisfactory for the level of quality we intended to achieve. CQI really demands an alteration in the way we look at things.

Whether we grew up in health care on the clinical or the administrative side, all of us routinely performed certain tasks. We would do a job based on the way we had seen someone else do it, or how we had been told to do it by a supervisor, or how we had habitually done it hundreds of times. Now, CQI's measurement and analysis tools were demanding that we not look at how something *had* been done, but rather learn to analyze what was effective and what wasn't.

We were counting on virtually hundreds of leaders throughout our facilities to set an example for the tentative and unwilling. No matter how many letters, speeches, visits, or videotape presentations we came up with, we knew we could not provide the day-to-day leadership on the front line in our facilities.

In the SSM Health Care System, as in many health care institutions, leaders have experienced the pressure to change on three fronts. We've been called on to change our own ways of working and relating to peers and employees. We simultaneously have been responsible for guiding changes through our institutions. And we have had not merely to maintain, but to advance our competitive positions in health care markets that are continuously in flux. Nothing is standing still.

In this environment, none of us can hope to know enough or do enough on our own to achieve the quality we strive for. If the command-and-control approach to health care leadership was ever effective, that time is certainly past. And if ever a leader was able to put an institution on automatic pilot and let it run, that time too is past. Effective leadership now depends on our willingness to accept change, on our pursuit of continuous learning, and on our commitment to teamwork.

The leadership in the SSM Health Care System has been alternately disappointing, puzzling, and encouraging as we've traveled the CQI path.

We cannot say that we have had more breakdowns in leadership at our facilities since the launching of CQI in 1990. Our disappointment is that—with what is available in terms of training, systems, and processes—we have not had more breakthroughs. Our disappointment, generally, has come from an unfulfilled expectation that all of the top leaders in our facilities would effectively champion the possibilities of CQI.

We expected that communication about the work we were doing at the system level of the organization would cascade freely throughout all of the entities, so that individuals at every level would experience the freedom of a new culture opening up and could accept the challenge to participate in it. In too many cases, that has not happened.

A telling example came from a woman in upper management who was new to the system and unfamiliar with CQI. When she attended her first CQI meeting with team leaders and her entity's leadership team, she said the situation was so threatening and the leaders were so defensive that she told her boss she would not attend another such meeting. She said that team leaders dreaded making their reports because of the way they were grilled about their project proposals and then put off.

Later, she started attending corporate meetings with system management team members. "It was a real education for me," she said. "Things were different, the interactions were a lot different and a lot of the CQI principles were used, and you could see it was in your daily life. You could feel that there was change going on."

In the spirit of subsidiarity, we've been extremely reluctant to go into our entities and ask for an accounting of how the message of change is conveyed. But it was our expectation that leaders in a health care system that has quite publicly invested itself in improving the quality of care and service it provides its customers would devote themselves to making sure that the message was conveyed to their constituents—patients, employees, and physicians. When that has not occurred, we have been left asking ourselves, "If they are not doing that, what *are* they doing?"

We have signs on the walls of our entities that say, "Patients are our first priority." But we have had to wonder how often the presidents of our entities interact with patients. As senior leaders, have the presidents gone to sit in the admitting area to see how our patients are being treated? Do they ask the admitting clerk, "What were you thinking about when you were talking to that patient?," "What was really the most important thing for you when you were having that transaction?," and "What impression do you think you left them with?" Without a leadership presence in the places where service and care get delivered, the whole idea of quality improvement seems suspect.

We have been told by some entity executives, directly and indirectly, that CQI adds too much work to their jobs. But we cannot always see meaningful results from whatever that work is.

The CQI principle that all work is part of a process applies to the work of leaders, too. The discipline of designing or redesigning processes really does open a new realm of effectiveness. Yet we still don't see across-the-board evidence that some of our top people are using the tools of process analysis that are right in front of them. Some people, seven years after CQI's launching, still define their jobs by tasks rather than processes.

A major difference between the mind-set of a task and that of a process is that tasks usually present themselves as something "I" need to do or "you" need to do, whereas with a process the focus is rightly placed on the steps necessary to achieve an end result with the least amount of time, waste, and rework. Viewing work as a process causes a person to envision the intended outcome and then plan how to get there with the resources available.

In the corporate office, if we defined our work as tasks that we had to do rather than as processes, we could be at work 24 hours a day. We're not masters in the skills of CQI yet by any means, but we have learned that when we define a process we can use our time managing the fulfillment of many processes, rather than doing task after task by ourselves.

# ARE WE DOING THE RIGHT THINGS?

We are reminded of the questions posed to us by quality consultants in 1989: Are you doing the right things? And are you doing them the right way?

Some recent statistics about the work of key people in health care shed light on the task orientation in our industry. One study showed that nurses perform 350 tasks, more than half of which could be done by someone who is unlicensed. When nurses define their jobs by specific tasks, rather than by the process of managing a patient's total care plan, it has to cost them something in terms of their professional satisfaction. And it also costs their patients in terms of the quality of care they receive.

Another study reported that 60 percent of what goes on in a physician's office does not have to be performed by a physician.

Those are just two examples, but they are useful because when we think of the leverage points where health care can be improved by the right processes, we have to think of physicians and nurses. By extension, we have to assume that there are many executives in our organizations who also are doing lots of tasks they don't need to do. We are concerned that they are defining themselves by those tasks rather than defining themselves as leaders, coaches, and mentors for the people around them.

If we go back before 1990, we remember that what was so appealing about CQI was that it gave us a very specific way to implement the values we have been talking about for years. We were saying, "Yes, we want to create this kind of organization, we just don't know how." Then we found a methodology and a way to implement our values in a concrete way. Now we have the disconnect of having a set of tools that allows people to implement our values and discovering that the tools aren't always used.

# FEAR IN THE WORKPLACE

With all of the changes our system has seen over the past seven years in terms of CQI implementation, acquisitions of health care facilities, the development of the St. Louis Health Care Network, and the functional and clinical integration within the network, we have not been shy about asking for an enormous contribution from our entity leaders.

But while we have been asking people to provide more leadership, some of them have interpreted this as a request for more work. We believe that part of this misinterpretation is due to fear—a fear of losing the thing that gives us a comfortable sense of identity and a hold on our place in the scheme of things.

Everything we have read and heard about change in the workplace warned us of the fear that is a natural human reaction. None of us in system management has been able to escape our confrontations with fear.

We didn't wake up one morning eager to face the uncertainties and criticism that change would bring, but we had prepared ourselves with learning. We persisted in moving through the fear.

When we brought in Kathleen Ryan to work with us, coauthor of *Driving Fear Out of the Workplace,*[1] Sister Mary Jean took the opportunity to be evaluated by the members of entity leadership. No one in his or her right mind could imagine that she relished the process or enjoyed hearing a critique of her leadership style. But as a leader, she was willing to be the first to take on a process that we thought would be valuable for every leader to undertake.

We asked that entity leaders take the process of evaluation back to their own institutions to open up some room for authentic communication among their leadership team. But that didn't happen. We believe our system is paying the price of that failure of leadership. Wherever leaders are stopped by their fear, they stop being leaders.

All leaders—at the highest levels of government or business or at the level of the individual—need to be willing to take risks, to be on the line for something, and to put the commitment to service or values ahead of concern for protecting their back. We suspect that if a leader is unwilling to open himself or herself to a candid evaluation by the people with whom they work most closely, that leader cannot be cultivating an atmosphere of freedom, communication, and teamwork.

Within our system management team, we have 10 highly trained, intelligent, and articulate people. We are men and women from diverse backgrounds, styles, and personalities. Our meetings together are not always pleasant, but they are productive. We have been training ourselves during the past seven years to be straightforward with one another. We have taken the pains and the time to learn how each of us thinks as part of our commitment to developing a real team.

We have taken on the transformation of ourselves from Lone Rangers and Mighty Mouses to partners and team players. By investing the effort, we have reaped results.

We see that we have failed in enrolling some of the leaders of our facilities to do similar work among themselves. At times we have been patient, and at other times we have just been exasperated.

Bill recalled attending a meeting of several facility leaders during which some thorny issues had to be worked through. *Two months* after that meeting, the person who had led it came to Bill with several criticisms from other people about the way he had acted at the meeting. He could not imagine what would have prevented real leaders to have spoken directly to him immediately after the fact if they had constructive criticism to offer.

Conversely, around the same time, an administrative assistant in another part of the corporate office had the courage and sense of partnership to go directly to Bill, face to face, with a complaint about something he had done the day before. Here was somebody with no title, no big salary, and no fiduciary responsibility for a multibillion dollar system, who was willing to stand for something and let the chips fall where they might.

Yes, there is a risk in being straight with people. It does not always make for a "nice" conversation. But something we have heard time and again from objective outsiders who have assisted us in breaking through some of our unproductive methods is that we are nice at the expense of producing the results we are committed to.

A person who had been in the system a long time said, "Gosh, you'll get fired if you speak up." Sister Mary Jean asked if that had ever happened, and the person said, "No, but it could."

Sometimes, in our frustration, we have told some groups of leaders that if we were going to start a new corporation tomorrow, one of the things a person would get fired for is not speaking up. Speaking up entails risk, but we will get nowhere if we cannot risk. If people think they are not going to make mistakes, they must not be doing anything.

If the people we have trusted enough to lead the health care institutions that make up the system are afraid to confront us with their complaints, express their doubts about CQI, ask questions, or acknowledge what they don't understand, how can they create a climate in which people who work with them are free to communicate?

On the other side, we realize that we have not pursued the issue. We have not gone to them and said, "It's okay if you have concerns. Let's talk about them, and if we cannot convince you that this is what needs to be done, then perhaps there is a better organization for you to work in." We still do not have a process in place to make sure those kinds of conversations happen.

Developing real leadership, as opposed to titular leadership, is ultimately a process of personal learning and risk taking. It cannot be imposed. It can only be assumed by people who are committed to something larger than their own safety.

> **T**hose in leadership positions have to be willing to put the spotlight on themselves to see where they are raising barriers to open communication, even if it takes bringing in someone from the outside to help.

## INFORMAL LEADERSHIP

As we've gone along, we have been inspired by many people who have begun to take up the challenge of leadership. A wonderfully surprising aspect of leadership in our system is that which is practiced, unbidden, by employees who have no executive titles. These are the people who move us with their magnificence.

A trauma nurse at Cardinal Glennon Children's Hospital took the initiative to implement a program to educate preschool children about the dangers of handguns. The president of Glennon didn't go to her and say, "We really need this program." It was just that after seeing the growing numbers of kids under five coming into the emergency department with gunshot wounds, she decided it was needed. She provided it.

A security guard at St. Marys Hospital Medical Center in Madison was on duty at the pay parking lot when a woman drove up to the exit gate and said she had been in the hospital to visit her husband and hadn't realized until leaving the lot that she had left her purse at home. The guard, who shared this with us in a letter, said she waved the woman through the gate and wished her a good day. The guard didn't check with her supervisor before taking action. She wrote that the day before, she had heard Sister Mary Jean give a talk about putting the customer first, and she felt that this was the perfect opportunity to do that.

Another example of unbidden leadership occurred in Cardinal Glennon Hospital's playroom. The young man who supervises the playroom saw a white mother pull her son away from an African-American boy and tell him they couldn't play together. The man went up to the mother and said that she and her son should leave the playroom because that kind of behavior wasn't acceptable. They left, and the young supervisor wondered if he would lose his job or be reprimanded for his action. The next day the mother brought her son back to playroom, willing to comply with the value that the supervisor had stood up for.

At St. Mary's Health Center in Richmond Heights, Missouri, where the implementation of patient-focused care raised a high level of anxiety and criticism among various sectors of the staff, a veteran nursing assistant told us that she thinks patient-focused care is wonderful. After working in the same job for 20 years, she said she now experiences being a partner in the total care of the patient and has a sense of being an equal with her coworkers. In the face of discontent about patient-focused care around the hospital, she goes around telling people how great it is.

Some people may doubt that these are examples of "real" leadership. We believe unequivocally that they are exactly what leadership is about. These types of actions define the *quality* of work and the *quality* of thinking that has to be present for a cultural transformation to occur, no matter how sophisticated the plan. Whether it is an innate or a developed trait, people who are real leaders—at whatever level in the organization—demonstrate the capacity to step out, show their colors, and spread the word.

Many others in supervisory and middle management positions showed their leadership when we first began CQI by coming forward to take on the responsibilities of being a team leader. They knew that team leader positions would be a temporary role and their former job would not be held for them, but they said, "I'm willing to take that on."

There was also a group of about 300 people, selected by their hospitals as informal leaders, who met with us at hands-on healers meetings. They are people that—regardless of the culture they work in and the type of supervisor, president, or vice president they have—always stand out among their peers.

The challenge for us is, how do we create environments that allow other people who have similar talents and abilities to shine? That's a place where we haven't made the cultural changes we would like to see.

When we were doing CQI training, we spent time with many bright, talented, capable employees who were engaged in educating their children, running church groups, leading Boy Scout and Girl Scout troops, and providing significant leadership in other activities. When these people come to work and are told things like "You can't approve buying a pencil" and "You have to check with your supervisor before you can leave your work area," they are not going to consider work a place where they can make a vibrant contribution.

An example of a practice that stifles employee initiative is putting unnecessary limits on the work of a quality team.

At one hospital a few years ago, a team designed a solution for the proper disposal of needles. As they were getting ready to implement it, the nursing director told them they couldn't do it until they had presented all of their findings and cost justified it. It was demoralizing to the team and put the lid on employee initiative and creativity.

Some of the initial CQI team charters had an area called "constraints." One hospital routinely used this constraint option to say, "No financial information will be shared unless it is approved by the administration." What does that communicate? Why are we saying people can't have access to information? Why does it have to be screened and monitored and checked?

*We in formal leadership have to look at the things we do almost automatically that demonstrate our lack of trust in people.*

## INSTITUTIONAL LEADERSHIP

In a system as large as ours, we expected mixed results with CQI. But what keeps our vision alive are the instances, individual and institutional, where we know that CQI is really working.

At St. Francis Hospital and Health Center in Blue Island, we've been impressed with the turnaround of an institution that had admittedly lost track of who it was serving as the area went from middle income to lower income. The president and the rest of the leadership team have worked to integrate all of the CQI concepts into the organization. It is becoming a patient-focused and market-sensitive operation.

The leaders of the St. Louis Health Care Network, which we will say more about later, brought the processes of CQI directly to the work of implementing a functional and clinical integration of 11 areas throughout seven health centers. Using CQI tools and teamwork, they were able to bring their plan from drawing board to reality within six months. In 1996, the scope of this integration was unparalled in the country.

St. Francis Hospital in Maryville, a small and unremarkable facility before 1989, was one of the first six entities to jump into CQI, and—with the leadership of a strong and undauntable president—it earned a Missouri Quality Award. St. Francis was cited for the large number of listening and learning posts established to find out the requirements, expectations, and satisfaction of patients and other stakeholders. The judges also noted that the senior leadership team promotes the values of the hospital and "is visible on a daily basis to reinforce the vision, values, and direction of the organization." Visibility and vision are keys to real leadership.

At St. Marys Hospital Medical Center in Madison, the vice president of patient care services, a nurse, took the initiative to reorganize the nursing departments using integrated teams. They developed a self-governing group, called a nursing council, that has taken responsibility for the major areas involving nurses. Members of the council chair committees relating to issues like nursing quality, nursing education, universal standards, and so on.

The Information Center, one of the businesses of the system's Shared Services, brought CQI principles to bear on the implementation of a new, systemwide information system. The leaders of the center brought together teams of people from every department in the system, using quality processes. They were able to reach a consensus on how to standardize all of the equipment and software and get it up and running without major breakdowns. The information system includes local area networks; wide area networks; access to external, governmental, and commercial databases; videoteleconferencing; teleradiology; and general telecommunications.

At DePaul Health Center, a St. Louis institution acquired by our system in 1995, a new president who moved up from within the hospital has used data gathered from customers by the St. Louis Healthcare Alliance to identify the areas at DePaul where quality needs to be improved. He has assembled teams and made sure they are aligned on the key objectives for improvement. He openly discusses issues with as many people in the hospital as possible, and he uses department head meetings as places where people can spend their time contributing to the actual solutions of problems rather than simply hearing more information.

This kind of leadership in our facilities is what creates a culture in which people can focus on how to make the organization better. We are more and more coming to understand how powerful the entity presidents are in shaping the culture of all of our organizations, even within the larger system.

## PROTECTING GROWTH

In evaluating the conditions that promote or hinder cultural transformation in our facilities, we saw a phenomenon that reminds us of how fragile a new culture can be. There are places in the system where the existing culture of a community, or a hospital, can absorb or overwhelm a leader. This cuts both ways as far as quality is concerned.

The quality culture of the facility at Maryville was deeply ingrained by the time president Ray Brazier left there in 1995 to be president of Hillcrest Health Center in Oklahoma. A new president trying to start a command-and-control structure would have met such significant resistance that he or she could not have succeeded. The quality culture under Ray was sufficiently embedded that the incoming president could provide quality leadership without having to swim against the current.

But at two other facilities, when new presidents came in from elsewhere, the fragile CQI cultures suffered. It wasn't necessarily that the new leaders openly opposed CQI, but they weren't champions for it.

A change of president when the CQI structure is fragile can devastate it. It may still be there, and people will still pay lip service to it, but the quality accomplishments won't show up.

> *In the early stages of any major change, the infrastructure really lives in the senior leaders. Losing the infrastructure damages the momentum of an organization.*

## MIDDLE MANAGEMENT

The group of people in the system for whom leadership and change has been most problematic is those in middle management. It is true not because of who the people are, but because of their positions.

Managers at this level are at risk in terms of losing their positions because their roles were poorly created years ago. We haven't provided opportunities for them either to explore other things or to offer a way to recreate their positions.

In the implementation of CQI, we intended for managers' roles to shift from that of directors and overseers to coaches and teachers. Rather than being the ones who know how to do everything and have all of the answers, managers would be asked to empower their employees to see their jobs as a series of processes and find ways to improve them.

Theoretically, this shift would take a burden off the manager. But sometimes managers find this threatening to their authority and position. This is especially true for middle managers because they are, by definition, straddling the roles of a person accountable for others' performance and a provider of some type of care or service—nurse, technician, dietitian, information specialist, and so on. They are asked to do a job they've been professionally trained for and also to manage others like themselves—a job for which they probably have not been trained. These positions are usually offered and accepted as an acknowledgment of the skill, competence, and reliability people have demonstrated in their original, frontline job.

In the managerial role, they don't have the same confidence to start with. The insecurity of being a "hybrid"—halfway between employee and administrator—and the two-pronged responsibilities of their technical work and managerial role make this group potentially the most reluctant to enthusiastically embrace the kinds of change that quality management demands.

This concern was highlighted during a meeting some of our managers had with people at the Wainwright Corporation, a Baldrige Award winner. One of Wainwright's executives was asked what the company's managers thought when employees got together to form a team to address customer issues. The executive's response was, "Why would the managers care?"

He was rhetorically asking, Why would managers care that groups of employees were getting together to improve services to the customer if that is precisely what the managers are supposed to be motivating their employees to do?

His response underlined the oddness of a managerial mind-set that sees a reason to be threatened by employees' taking initiative. But that mind-set exists in our entities—and, we suspect, in many other hospitals as well.

With the introduction of teams, team leaders, facilitators, and projects, middle managers would logically wonder about their place in the new order. So we asked the entity leaders to reassure the managers of their essential leadership role in CQI. They wouldn't be responsible for creating all of the solutions or ideas, but they would be relied on to communicate and carry out new processes within and across departments.

To empower this to happen, we asked that managers and supervisors always be trained in CQI skills at the same time as their employees. Teams were asked to keep managers informed of their progress on projects. And managers were invited to become team facilitators. In some entities, these managers took on the team leader's role for a project. As a team leader, a manager or supervisor can become accustomed to working more as a coach than as an overseer.

Still, our middle managers are having to resolve with their own teams the questions for which there are no textbook answers.

- How does a manager who is not on a team with his or her employees give or receive input?

- What is a manager supposed to do when a team is determining what the manager's job will consist of?

- If a manager can solve a problem faster on his or her own, should it really be taken to a QIT to solve?

- How do you strike a balance between faithfulness to the CQI process, meeting the work objectives, and watching the bottom line?

*An organization has to learn to recognize the people who have leadership potential and support them in assuming greater degrees of responsibility.*

*People selected to be managers need more than competence in a special area. They need to be leaders.*

····································

*Leadership has shown up in the SSM Health Care System in places where we would not ordinarily have looked. If we emphasize leadership as a function of titles or responsibility, we lose the contributions of hundreds of leaders throughout the system.*

## Note

1. Kathleen D. Ryan and Daniel K. Oestreich, *Driving Fear Out of the Workplace* (San Francisco: Jossey-Bass Publishers, 1991).

# 5

# INFUSING A CUSTOMER FOCUS INTO THE SYSTEM

*Having a customer orientation is much more than "customer service." In the second phase of CQI we learned that a focus on the customer becomes operational only through strategic planning.*

························

The three phases of the system's CQI implementation were intended to provide a logical progression of learning and participation for managers and employees at every level.

By starting with quality teams, each entity would have the opportunity to train both administrative and clinical staff in CQI tools and principles. Then each team would work to improve a process identified by the entity steering team. We believed this would give visibility to the teams, demonstrate that CQI was a practical hands-on effort, and provide some measurable accomplishments. This decision was also based on the fact that traditionally in health care there has been a lack of cross-functional work. Some of the first quality teams would break through this artificial separation by assembling employees from different departments to work together to improve processes.

The second phase, quality in strategic financial planning, was slated to begin well into the third year of implementation. After initiating broad involvement by the teams, the entities would strive for depth by infusing a customer focus into their long-range plans.

With CQI teams up and running and with strategic planning in place, we envisioned the third phase, quality in daily work life, emerging through both channels. Team members would bring their training and experience into every process and managers would consistently employ a CQI approach, basing decisions on data from patients, other customers, and the marketplace.

Some organizations that implemented quality efforts came to believe, in retrospect, that they should have started with planning rather than with teams. The planning process, they said, impels the organization to identify customers and their needs first and to base priorities on that data. Although we wouldn't necessarily change the order of our CQI phases, we do think that using more customer data in phase I would have stimulated team projects that were directly linked to customer satisfaction and process improvement.

We now are able to see some limitations to our initial approach with CQI teams. And we can share some of the insights we've gained about how the teams were set up.

At the launching of phase I, we emphasized process over results. We said, "If it takes a year to finish a project, that's fine." The effect of that statement was to leave teams with a virtually open-ended charter. The result was too much time spent on projects that achieved only incremental improvements.

If we were to go back and do it again, we would be much more aggressive in putting teams together and saying, "We want this team to achieve a specific result. We want to achieve a 50 percent improvement in medication errors [or a 50 percent improvement in patient wait times]." We would tell the teams they have three months or six months to achieve the improvement.

Some disillusionment with CQI, not only in our system but also in other organizations, has occurred because it has taken teams too long to produce significant improvements.

We began by saying that gradual improvements would be okay because we wanted to emphasize the continuous nature of the improvement process. We didn't want people to think that there would be one big push for improvement and that would be the end of it. Part of our reasoning, also, was that we didn't want to put pressure on the early teams who were unfamiliar with the tools and techniques of CQI. We thought it was important to give the teams time to get used to working together. And, in fact, that *was* important. It just need not have taken so long.

The seven-step CQI model that we developed with Paul Plsek was designed to ensure that a team would really look at the process being used and get to the root cause of the problem, rather than jumping quickly to a conclusion. Going through the seven steps is useful, but by not emphasizing the need to achieve a significant result in a short time period, the process becomes tedious and teams get bogged down. Valuable people spending one hour a week together for several months and only improving processes by 10 percent or 5 percent wasn't a satisfactory return.

As a result of garnering only small results, the seven-step model gained a bad reputation. But we're convinced that there is nothing wrong with the model itself. The problem was the slowness with which teams worked through it. There is a natural cautiousness when people are learning to go through a new process. If those of us who were responsible for setting the pace for the first teams—the teachers, facilitators, team leaders, and entity steering teams—had allowed for the learning curve but also had set clear limits in terms of results and deadlines, it would have stimulated teams to be more assertive and creative in their solutions.

Laying down the challenge of producing a substantive result within a deadline eliminates the option of nibbling around the edges of a problem. If team members know they have a limited time to come up with a significant process improvement, they become more innovative. They start thinking outside of the box.

A few of our entities have begun to push teams for faster turn-arounds and bigger results by participating in the Breakthrough Series, sponsored by the Institute for Healthcare Improvement (IHI).

The IHI breakthrough concept assists organizations in having their commitment to quality produce specific actions and concrete results. The goal is to improve medical outcomes, satisfaction, and access while lowering costs.

The model of the Breakthrough Series is based on three questions.

1. What are we trying to accomplish?
2. How will we know if a change is an improvement (especially from the customer's viewpoint)?
3. What change could we try that we believe will result in improvement?

The arenas of the initial work in the Breakthrough Series included C-section rates, adult intensive care, reducing delays and wait times, and outpatient asthma care.

Breakthrough brings in more people at the start of a project than would normally be on a QI team. This larger group of people, 20 or so, puts a lot of ideas on the table both as probable causes for the problem at hand and as possible solutions. The smaller team then takes the ideas and uses problem-solving steps to test for the real root cause and match a solution with it. In a way, this could be seen as jump starting the improvement process. A large group brainstorms, then a smaller team studies, designs, measures, and refines.

Typically, the improvement process suggested by IHI in its Breakthrough Series has three bases for identifying a result. One is an arbitrary formula that calls for a large improvement in a short time, such as achieving a 50 percent reduction in the occurrence of a problem by the end of six months.

The second is a result suggested by the customers themselves. For example, a facility could survey emergency department patients and ask them what an acceptable waiting period would be. If the survey indicates that the majority of respondents said a 30-minute wait is acceptable, then the team would set that time as the initial objective.

A third way to set a goal for a breakthrough would be to look at the best practice in the industry. For example, what is the shortest average emergency wait time in the country? If one of our facilities decided to benchmark—a practice in which our system so far has not excelled—it could either try to match the process used by the benchmarked institution, or it could simply use the best time as a goal and design its own process.

Since 1995, six of our hospitals and the St. Louis Health Care Network have started teams on at least one Breakthrough Series project. Two examples of success so far are St. Mary's Health Center in Richmond Heights, which reduced by 50 percent the elapsed time between an admission decision made in the emergency department and the patient's arrival in the room; and St. Francis Hospital at Blue Island, which reduced the time between a patient's discharge by the physician and his or her actual departure by 56 percent.

Our participation in the Breakthrough Series is part of a commitment to accelerate all of our CQI team work. By having various facilities sign up for Breakthrough Series projects that correlate with their priorities, employees are receiving training they can carry over to other projects as well.

We intend for the Breakthrough Series work to instill a greater desire for excellence throughout the organization. It should push us to look outward to some of the best practices of other institutions.

Both of us have at times become discouraged over the institutional mind-set that says, "We're good enough if we have 95 percent compliance with standards." When challenged to go a little further, some people in the system will say, "Well, you don't understand why we can't be better." When we hear these kinds of conversations at the highest levels of the organization, we can be sure they are happening at other levels as well.

There are people who know intellectually that more can be done to improve, but achieving it takes a willingness to interrupt both a personal and institutional complacency.

If people in an institution continually encourage and spur one another on, the work of change may not be any less arduous, but it will get done. On the other hand, if leaders keep hearing their coworkers or employees ask, "How much more can you expect us to do?", it is much easier for the leader to back off than to keep pushing.

The cultural transformation demanded by a commitment to continuous improvement occurs in an organization only when a sufficient number of people are willing to spur themselves and others out of complacency. This seems to be one of the primary values of having a common mission and working as a team to achieve it.

We began with the idea that forming teams to take on manageable improvement projects would lead to some early successes. These successes would in turn motivate an interest in more challenging projects, and a momentum would develop. Although this has occurred in some cases, it has not happened yet to the extent we thought it would.

We believe that if just half of the people in the system's institutions were involved in projects where they made a significant improvement (or even a small improvement) in their jobs, it could create the critical mass that turns the tide. Somewhere in the scheme of an organization, however, the ideal of innovation gets bogged down.

In some instances, it might be a coworker who says to another, "Let's just keep cleaning the floors the way we have; it will take too long to find another way." Then the employee who wants to bring some ingenuity to the task is squelched. In other instances, it may be department heads who have a chilling effect on innovation by putting down or putting off employees who are enthusiastic about new ideas.

What motivates people to work better? What gets people excited about finding new solutions to problems? Those are questions that still puzzle us more than seven years after the start of CQI.

## STRATEGIC FINANCIAL PLANNING

A small group from the system management team, plus representatives from the entities and an outside consultant, spent 1992 researching and designing the system's strategic financial planning process for phase II of CQI.

We did not want to have a strategic planning process for the system and then, additionally, have a "quality planning process." We wanted to bring it all into one process, so that our strategic plan was not saying one thing while our quality principles said another.

Several of us in system management did a lot of work in the development of the planning process, talking with boards, entity leaders, and planning and finance experts to make the structure user-friendly and flexible enough that all of the entities—from the largest to the smallest—could use it consistently.

The basis for our planning model is called the Organization As a System (OAS), developed by Thomas W. Nolan (of Associates in Process Improvement) and Paul Batalden, M.D. OAS is a way of focusing on and integrating the concepts of process, customers, communities, and planning for improvements. It is based on the Deming theory that you have to understand what you do, why you do it, and how to improve it. OAS gives planners a framework for understanding the customer-community-quality-process connection.

We developed a five-day training course for volunteer coaches who were to go back to their entities and assist their administrative staffs or planning teams through the process. Coaches included entity presidents, quality resource managers, marketing, finance, and operations people.

The plan was approved by the system's board of directors in March 1993 and was piloted in the first year by three facilities. When these first teams submitted their two-year plans to the corporate office in October 1993, the design team reviewed their work to see what we needed to refine before beginning phase II systemwide in January 1994. Then, after an entire year of systemwide experience, we issued a revised planning implementation manual in October 1995. The entire process was in keeping with the PDCA cycle of continuous improvement.

Bringing CQI to strategic financial planning requires finding out who our customers are and what they want, then using that data as the basis for buy decisions about operational improvements, capital expenditures, new programs, and so on. In 1995, as a major change in the process, we named five categories of quantifiable progress indicators. The categories are clinical and community health, customer satisfaction (including physician and employees satisfaction), operational objectives, financial performance, and the ways the organization has changed.

Within the planning cycle, an entity looks at all of the customer satisfaction and market trend data, assesses its resources to see how much can be done, and then selects the key indicators around which quantifiable improvements will be made.

The highly programmed structure of this strategic planning process compels the entities to collect data about their market areas, their customers, and the level of customer satisfaction. We assured planners that the data gathered from customer surveys, focus groups, and patient satisfaction surveys would not replace the traditional data regarding competition, market trends, and technology. But now we were going to fold in direct feedback from patients and other customers and from our service areas so that plans could include specific themes and action steps aimed at satisfying, or even delighting, the people we served.

In the first full year of strategic planning, and even in the second year for some, the entity plans still tended more toward analysis than toward specific actions. We were looking for submissions that said, "As a result of the analysis we've been doing, here are three things we are going to work on next year and these are the quantifiable results that we will produce." Instead, we received plans that said, "Next year, we will analyze and evaluate the possibility of doing XYZ."

Part of the difficulty in achieving the results we envisioned was that virtually everyone working to develop the entity plans was new to the process. Even those who were coaching others had only five days of classroom experience.

We might have circumvented the problem of inexperience if the six of us who were facilitators for the pilot entities had stayed more directly and visibly involved through the first year's work. We could have met with individual planning teams for one or two sessions and talked about what to look for, or we could have had more interaction with the coaches through conference calls. In the end, we really left it up to the individual entities. We gave them a contact person, but we did not establish a schedule for checking in to see what problems had arisen.

With two rounds of systemwide, customer-focused planning behind us—as this is being written—we believe we are now on track to focus on key customer measures such as cost, satisfaction, and quality of care. As basic as this focus may seem from a quality perspective and as humbling as it may be to admit, in the American health care tradition, measures of customer satisfaction have *not* been uppermost in management's mind.

One of our larger facilities, St. Francis Hospital and Health Center in Blue Island, identified this shortcoming fairly early in its planning process and has begun doing a better job of learning about the customer. The administrative team at St. Francis recognized that the hospital was losing contact with its community. The area had had a large influx of Hispanic people, and St. Francis was slow to respond to that change. It had became disconnected from its customers. With the planning process, the leaders realized that they had to identify who was in their service area and find out what those residents wanted.

Another entity in the system, the St. Louis Healthcare Network, had to resubmit its plan in 1995 and came back with a much greater customer focus. The network also included a portfolio of measurable results it is working toward. These examples give us hope that even if progress isn't rapid, a new planning muscle is being developed by our institutions.

Planning requires looking down the road, envisioning potential scenarios, and determining the best course to take in any eventuality. But a common characteristic of health care professionals is a preference for reacting rather than planning. We've seen a reluctance among some managers to create a plan and follow it. Instead, they deal with the problem of the day. If there are employee relations problems, they handle those and let other performance indicators slip. If there are financial problems this month, they focus on those.

A strategic plan—based on objective data—takes creativity, energy, and quick wittedness. Nonplanners will say, "If they do that, we'll do this. But if they do something else, then we'll react this way." Reactive managers operate from the belief that if they don't know what is going to happen, they won't know what to do until it happens. That, however, is not the way strategic planning works.

If we are committed to superior performance in all aspects of our institutions, then we can't sacrifice employee relations to finance or sacrifice quality to make a doctor happy. We have to manage the entire process. This isn't a matter of doing one thing or another; it is a matter of doing it all. But if you want to do it all, no individual or small group can handle it. You have to mobilize the entire organization.

A key element of building a CQI environment is, as Deming referred to it, "constancy of purpose." If leaders are always reacting to issues, there is no commitment to a strategy. And if leaders do not commit to a strategy and pursue it aggressively, then the organization has no direction. A balance between reacting when necessary and being committed to a course is ideal—but if in health care the pendulum swings farther to one side than another, it is in favor of reaction rather than steadfastness.

# THE INTERNAL AND EXTERNAL PUSH FOR QUALITY

In system management and in most of our facilities, we now realize that measures of customer satisfaction are what we must keep our eye on. Managing so as to move those key measures in the right direction is our primary job.

This realization has come in part from our integration of CQI principles with our strategic planning. And it also has been motivated by an outside source, the St. Louis Healthcare Quality Alliance—a group of employers, hospital representatives, and insurance representatives that began conducting comparative studies of area hospitals a few years ago.

By late 1996, health care consumers in our system's largest market would have the ability, for the first time, to make side-by-side comparisons of all of the area hospitals. The hospitals were to be rated in about 20 different categories as "better than expected," "as expected," or "worse than expected" on the basis of clinical and customer surveys.

Public evaluation is a new element for hospitals to deal with, and it brings with it a certain anxiety. Every institution wants to be well-ranked, including those in the SSM Health Care System. But we will not be surprised if some of our facilities, like others in this large hospital market, receive some low ratings in customer service. The health care industry simply has not seen itself as a customer service provider in the way that the hotel, restaurant, and airline industries have.

When patients' opinions about hospital costs and the quality of service and care they receive in various institutions are made public, these should serve as wake-up calls. As unpleasant as criticism might be, the institutions that are interested in quality ought to welcome it. It gives us a chance to see where we can do better and where we can distinguish ourselves.

We have two concerns about comparisons among a community's hospitals, however. Certainly, customers' appraisals of the quality of service they receive in our facilities can be highly instructive. But given the health care industry's poor track record as a customer service business, it would not be wise to gauge ourselves against the performance of other health care institutions.

Even the hospitals that are striving mightily for excellence still need to learn more about what excellence really is. To do that, we need to investigate many kinds of service businesses that consistently delight their customers. One of the worst possible things we could do in health care is compare ourselves to ourselves before there is enough excellence in customer service anywhere to bother talking about. For example, if one of the SSM Health Care System's hospitals received a high quality rating compared to another area hospital, it would not tell us much about how we are doing on the scale of real excellence. And similarly, if a hospital received a lower rating, it would be a mistake to think that when we can match numbers with the higher-rated hospital we will be excellent. To be able to say "We're as good as so-and-so" is not good enough, and if we only have that mentality we will never achieve the quality we are committed to.

Our second concern is that hospital evaluations will be published with a flurry, but once the publicity dies down there will still not be a long-term, internal push for radical improvements.

For more than seven years, we have heard from people within the SSM Health Care System who actively resist the possibility that cost-effectiveness, quality, and service could all improve at the same time. We have responded to such resistance by acknowledging that, inside of the customary paradigms of health care, it is true.

For example, bringing down the cost of patient bedside care without redesigning the *method* of bedside care probably is not possible. The challenge we face in a customer-oriented industry, as opposed to a technology-oriented or a staff-oriented industry, is to design the processes so that there can be both better quality and more effective deployment of resources.

We hear from some groups in the system that we should keep doing things in a particular way because that is the way it worked in the past. We also hear that we should keep people in the same jobs because it is not fair to ask them to do something else. But the health care marketplace will not tolerate that. Some jobs that were created during a time of high inpatient volume and sophisticated tertiary care must be eliminated or redefined.

The pressure for low-cost performance means that we have to look beyond the way we've always done things. We cannot both bring down costs and improve service by continuing to do things in the traditional way.

The possibility created by bringing a customer orientation into strategic planning is that solutions for better cost-effectiveness, service, and quality really must be integrated with the institution's spending, hiring, and investment decisions. Yes, this is extremely challenging, because it demands real innovation and creativity. But it also gets to the heart of transforming a culture.

## BREAKING THROUGH BARRIERS TO CHANGE

We never expected a smooth road to continuous quality. But neither did we expect that it would take some of the system's employees to the brink of mutiny. In chapter 6, we look at one of the most controversial redesigns we have undertaken, patient-focused care. In the two locations it has been tried to date, it has been unsuccessful. But we have not given up on its premise. We consider it to be the truest example of a redesign that so far has come out of CQI.

In the traditional way of operating within health care, the hospital would revert to the old way if a new approach or system failed. With our commitment to redesigning care so that it is focused on the patient or other customers, that will not happen. When particular changes don't work, teams can go back to the drawing board—but that doesn't mean going back to the old way.

One of our courses is designed to help team leaders break through conventional approaches to problem solving. When Bill taught the course, he would ask participants for an example of something that they knew irritated or inconvenienced patients. Participants would cite something like the complaint that it takes two hours to get through routine presurgical tests.

Bill would have the team leaders verbally go through the process of the tests, step by step. They begin with registration at the admitting office, moving to a room for an EKG, moving to another room for an X-ray, going to another room for laboratory tests, and then going to a cashier to pay or fill out insurance forms. The class exercise, then, is to redesign the process of presurgical testing, with no constraints except that all of the tests be done within 15 minutes.

What the team leaders discover is that there is no way the process can be reduced to 15 minutes if they stay inside of the established framework. No matter how quickly a radiologist or a phlebotomist or anyone else works, it would take a complete reorganization of the testing steps to reduce the time from two hours to a quarter of an hour.

But what if one person in one location were trained to do the paperwork for an admission, take an X-ray, do an EKG, and draw blood? Each step would take only as much time as the real process actually takes. There would be no time spent walking from one place to another, and no hand-offs from one person to another. This kind of change is not about accelerating the existing process— leaving everything the same but somehow making it move in quadruple time—it is about changing the paradigm in which the process takes place.

It is this kind of out-of-the-box thinking that teams focused on the customer must develop. How could we make life easier for patients? Are our hours of business convenient to the patient, or to us? Are we staffed according to when we want to work, or according to when we have the most customers coming through the doors? Do our shift changes accommodate the employees, or the customers?

We've both experienced those "moments of truth" as users of the system's hospitals when we wondered whether customers are the focus of the system. Those moments are snapshots that give a picture of how employees relate to customers in routine interactions. Employees may be efficient and polite—but if they leave the customer feeling unwelcome, confused, or in the way, it is doubtful he or she will want to come back, especially if there are a number of choices in the marketplace.

Integrating a cultural change that puts patients and other customers first is truly a much bigger job than we could have imagined in 1990. It has become clear to both of us, as well as to others in system management, that we have been working inside the old culture of health care just as everyone else has.

We can now consider the possibility that a good part of our first seven years of continuous quality improvement was spent becoming aware of the questions, issues, and barriers that we didn't even know were there, particularly regarding our orientation to customers.

For example, we find ourselves asking questions about the processes we have for recruiting and selecting people for various jobs based on our relatively new understanding of health care as a customer service business. Without that understanding, it made sense that human resource staffs would be hiring for education, experience, and/or demonstrated competence in the tasks of the position. But when we go out to look at *other* customer-oriented companies, we notice that they spend a lot more time and energy recruiting for their front lines men and women whose demonstrated competence also includes relating to people!

While traveling recently, Bill informally interviewed a flight attendant on an airline known for its friendly service. He wanted to find out how the airline managed to hire employees who were so engaging. The flight attendant told him that, except for pilots and mechanics and a few other people hired for very specific skills and experience, everyone else who seeks employment at the airline has to go through interviews in groups of 15 or 20. Five supervisors interview people in the group—not only listening to the answers, but watching how other people respond when an individual is answering.

The supervisors are looking for people who are engaged with whomever is talking. People who don't pay attention to the speaker get scratched from the list of candidates. The only ones who get called back for a second interview are those whom all five interviewers agree should be called back. In the second round, the candidate goes through individual interviews with five people, and again all five have to say, "Yes, this is the person we want to hire." This process is quite different from hiring practices in health care.

Specialization in hospitals has led to a focus on managers and supervisors who are skilled in a clinical or administrative competency, and they in turn hire people with similar skills. But as we walk through our facilities—or better yet, actually use the services of these facilities—we can see dozens of places where a more important emphasis should be on people.

Our emergency department clerks, admitting personnel, dietary clerks, housekeepers, and others have constant interaction with patients and can really make a big difference in how people perceive their treatment in the hospital. They can actually do the little things that make a person's stay pleasant, such as calling patients by name and asking how they are feeling.

Because we have not as a culture seen ourselves as customer focused, it has been sufficient for those doing the hiring to look for people who were like themselves or who had personalities pleasing to the one hiring. That is an example of a staff orientation rather than a customer orientation.

Neither of us is the kind of upbeat, gregarious personality that a customer-focused organization would put on its front lines of service—and our responsibilities don't demand that. If we were the ones hiring hospital admitting clerks, it would not be smart for us to look for people like ourselves. Yet we are afraid that this is what people in the system's institutions have too often done.

The question that our personnel managers must ask about those who have pivotal roles in the public places of our facilities is not "How do I feel about this person?" but rather "How will this person work with our patients and other customers?"

In a customer-focused business, that is what's important.

........................................

*It takes many kinds of people with different talents to perform the work of a health care system. Planning for a customer-focused business includes paying attention to the placement of the people who work where our patients and other customers interact with us.*

# 6

# TRANSFORMING THE CULTURE OF PATIENT CARE

*The profession of nursing has always been at the center of institutional care. It makes sense that major changes in health care would impact nurses most profoundly.*

......................................

Two challenging issues in the effort to build a quality culture in the SSM Health Care System have been, first, how to continuously improve patient care; and second, how to empower the key caregivers in our institutions.

Both of us, one a former nurse and the other married to a nurse, have compassion and understanding for today's nurses. Current conditions in the health care industry and in the nursing profession have created a climate of uncertainty. Patient bedside care has been changing dramatically since reimbursements have decreased, hospital stays have grown shorter, and acuity has heightened.

It's not surprising, given its predominant role in health care, that nursing would be a lightning rod. Changing care methods, new processes, and different staffing patterns, impact caregivers—often in ways not welcomed.

# PATIENT-FOCUSED CARE MISSTEPS AND LEARNINGS

In the SSM Health Care System, miscommunications and misperceptions about changes in patient care have resulted in some unrest among nurses and other employees.

At two of the system's hospitals, attempts were made to interrupt the status quo and implement a total redesign of bedside care. This redesign, called *patient-focused care,* is a genuine innovation that puts the patient at the center of a team of care providers. The team, led by a registered nurse, puts together a care plan for the patient. Members are cross-trained so that they are able to provide patients a range of basic services, in addition to providing the special services in which they are skilled.

This team approach helps to break down artificial barriers that hinder the flow of patient care services. For example, with patient-focused care, a respiratory therapist who has been taught how to give patients their food trays is able to assist in the process of distributing meals, rather than letting them cool on a food cart while one person delivers the trays.

At St. Mary's Health Center in Richmond Heights, patient-focused care was undertaken in a deliberate and slow-paced manner, with much attention paid to education and communication. But the timing for implementing this major change was poor. The hospital was also concentrating on making managerial changes and reducing costs. When patient-focused care was introduced, it proved too much for the organization to assimilate at one time.

At the other location, St. Francis in Blue Island, the decision was made to implement patient-focused care within six months. That approach did not work well either. Some early decisions got the project off on the wrong foot. The team then not only had to implement change, but also had to try to fix the ensuing problems. When some managerial jobs were eliminated too early, the team discovered it did not have enough support for fixing the problems and making the changes.

The two entities had hired different consulting companies, both of which had a good understanding of the structure of redesign but did not have a sufficient relationship with the cultures in which they were working. People who worked closely on the implementation told us that the organization itself should have addressed what patient-focused care would mean within its culture. A primary misstep was the failure to communicate the connection between the structural change called for by patient-focused care and its relationship to our mission and values.

Because the change called for a massive redeployment of staff, it became a source of uncertainty and insecurity for nurses and other employees. As a result, "patient-focused care" became a sort of rallying cry against change, even by people who hadn't had direct experience with it.

We knew going in that patient-focused care would be difficult for some people to accept. Seeing how difficult it was made us realize that mistakes had been made in communicating about this major change. From our perspective, there was a disproportionate gap between the viability of the idea and the resistance it provoked. Just as with the seven-step CQI model, we are convinced that the problem is not in the concept itself, but in certain aspects of its implementation.

In this case, we saw that disconnects in the system tend to occur in how we manage change between point A, the time of design, and point B, the time something is up and running smoothly. We have now tried twice to implement patient-focused care, in two different ways, and have not been successful.

Without yet knowing how patient-focused care will be reinstituted in system facilities, we have confidence in its value and believe that a quality culture needs more—not fewer—of these types of breakthrough efforts. Patient-focused care represents one of the few real redesigns that the system has tried. It requires staff to look at the hospital patient from an entirely new perspective. Unfortunately, this new perspective sheds glaring light on the degree to which the patient has *not* been at the center of care.

As a learning organization, we had to ask what have we learned from the early experience with patient-focused care. We have learned the following:

*It is impossible to overcommunicate.*

*The process of communication is a disciplined function that should bring people along, let new ideas simmer, and allow people the time to understand why change has to be made.*

*Communication needs to include not only what we are doing, but also why we are doing it, what the implications are, and where the rough spots will be.*

*We should not implement several simultaneous changes that overly stress the entire organization.*

# A NEW DIRECTION FOR NURSES

Some nurses in the system's facilities have had a difficult time accepting that their role is changing. They want things to be the way they were 10 or 20 years ago.

We are concerned when we hear nurses say things like, "The things that make me a nurse are my ability to take a pulse, blood pressure, temperature, and respiration." That is a limited—and we think questionable—view of what a nurse is. Certainly nurses are experts at monitoring patients' vital signs. But nursing assistants also are trained to do those things quite competently; in fact, those tasks are the substance of their job.

A slogan that has shown up around a few of our facilities is that "Every patient deserves a nurse." We agree, if that means every patient is entitled to a professional nurse with the judgment and skill to oversee care, accurately assess the patient's condition, and coordinate the provision of all the services a patient needs. But the idea that nurses should do all of the tasks themselves is a fallacy that has grown up around the profession.

Another saying that seems to have validity is, "The first person patients want to see when they wake up from surgery is a nurse." But this generalization doesn't distinguish the real need. What patients want when they wake up is a caring, attentive person who can supply what is needed to make them comfortable. That person *may* be a nurse, but it does not *need* to be.

It is disheartening to us that some nurses relinquish their most crucial positions as the designers of patient care plans and fail to expand their learning in a direction that will enhance their role and improve the quality of care.

For example, we have not yet seen many nurses who have taken on mentoring and coaching other care providers and enrolling them in finding better ways to fulfill the care effort. Assuming this kind of leadership is part of the self-development that we would expect of the primary caregivers in a patient-oriented culture.

Nurses who want to do only the familiar, hands-on work may be able to keep doing so. But in the long term, we seriously question that they will be considered professional nurses or be paid as professional nurses. The growth opportunities in nursing are as nurse practitioners, nurse educators, care planners, and case managers. These are roles that call for thinking, initiative, creativity, and, yes, risk taking.

The nurses who have four years, six years, even eight years of education will be the key clinical people in our hospitals and in the community. The demand will be for nurses who can think systemically about the patient and determine how all of the care issues interrelate, so that the appropriate actions can be taken. We are already seeing this level of nursing sophistication in outpatient practices, clinics, and home health care, where the physician's direct guidance is not immediately available. This also is where patient care is headed within the hospital.

Nurses who assume responsibility for groups of patients, both as inpatients and outpatients, will be valuable resources who can work with numerous caregivers. These professionals will realize that the inpatient component is just a small part of the integrated care that people need. Instead of having just a snapshot from the bedside, these nurses will know the whole person. They will be working with others to educate and create preventive plans so that people can stay out of the hospital if possible. They will take time to interview their patients and learn the whole scope of the situation so that the best overall care can be provided.

Instead of trying to anchor a safe and secure position in a status quo operation, people will have to develop themselves to think outside of the box. That isn't easy for system management and it isn't easy for nurses, but no one is exempt from that challenge. Even if those nurses who leave the SSM Health Care System do find a "traditional" institution to turn to, the security will not last long.

## NURSING LEADERSHIP

Most nurses would probably agree that nursing has not grown in clinical and administrative influence proportionate to its importance. Many nurses who want to exercise greater leadership have moved into more advanced practice roles outside of hospitals or into administrative posts, or have left health care altogether.

We believe that one condition reining in nursing leadership is the false premise that everyone with the initials "RN" after her or his name has comparable training. That is simply not true.

The national nursing organizations continue to recognize every type of program as if all are equal—two-year, three-year, bachelor's, and master's programs. These associations have so far been unwilling to say, "To ensure better quality of care, these are the criteria that every nurse must meet before taking an entry-level position as an RN." Right now, graduates of any program can say, "I am a nurse." They are *not* all equal, yet no one in nursing leadership seems willing to acknowledge that.

As a partial consequence of this wide spectrum of credentials, not all nurses are granted the respect or salaries they may be due. It doesn't make sense to us that someone with a master's degree would be paid the same as someone with an RN degree from a two-year program. Yet to justify a pay differential among employees who all have the same initials after their name, there would need to be objective standards of experience and responsibility. We think that by not demanding a stricter internal standard among nurses, the nursing profession has left itself vulnerable to questions—especially from others, like physicians, who *do* have to meet such a standard.

## THE UNION QUESTION

Some nurses think that major changes in their profession are not in their best interests and have become persuaded that union organization is the antidote to unwelcome change.

There also seems to be a belief that union membership will help guarantee job security for more nurses and that more nurses will improve the quality of care. This assumes that quantity ensures quality. We don't believe that more nurses will answer the difficult question of how to redesign patient care to increase quality and reduce the waste of human and material resources.

Union organizing among nurses began to emerge more strongly with the introduction of CQI. Unions of all types traditionally have objected to teams working to solve problems, because teams bring management and labor together. The first time Sister Mary Jean spoke in Canada about CQI, she referred to the compatibility of CQI principles and principles of Catholic social teaching regarding fairness to employees. Someone in the audience asked if CQI was not just a way to keep unions out of our system. This was the first she had ever heard of such an objection to CQI. But in Canada, where more nurses belong to unions than in the United States, implementing CQI teams has been difficult because of fear that the lines between management and labor will fade.

From many comments made to us and to the Quality Research Center, we have learned that when people begin participating in earnest on teams, they begin to see the possibilities of CQI. Where physicians, nurses, technicians, clerical workers, and others have adopted a team spirit—even if the team does not follow the seven-step model to a T—there is a shift in how they approach their work.

Teamwork for some nurses—just as for some physicians and health care managers—is not a part of the customary repertoire. CQI principles, tools, and skills have to be learned and practiced.

Those in any organization who don't adopt and familiarize themselves with a new way of working will eventually begin to feel like outsiders looking in. This is something with which not only nurses, but others among us as well, are grappling. To the degree that employees perceive they cannot affect key decisions in the workplace through the channels that exist, they disengage and may look outside the organization. Unfortunately, we think this is where union organizing among nurses starts to gain a foothold.

## NURSES AND FCI

In chapter 7, we will describe some of the work done to implement the functional clinical integration (FCI) of hospitals in the St. Louis Health Care Network. A lesson was learned there that specifically illuminates an issue with nurses in the SSM Health Care System.

Part of the integration project involved the reorganization of administrative teams, including the restructuring of nursing management. The plan developed would have eliminated the nursing vice presidents at each entity and established, instead, a nursing executive at the network level.

In keeping with an intent to have more democratic representation on the implementation team, the FCI planning team decided to bring nurses onto the team who were not in managerial positions. What was implicit in this decision was also a consideration that some of the nursing vice presidents in the network's hospitals would be resistant to the change and would "overly influence" the process.

Later, when we asked two of our nursing vice presidents from outside the central region to evaluate the FCI implementation, they told us that it had been a mistake to leave out nursing administrators. They said that by doing so, the FCI team had failed to avail itself of the knowledge of people who knew how to manage nursing services. In other words, the decision didn't reflect the CQI principle of involving the people with the best knowledge of the process.

With 20-20 hindsight, we could see that everyone on the team had been so anxious about the impact of the changes FCI would cause and the nursing managers' anticipated reaction that the team's thinking had been clouded. Upon realizing this, the FCI team got input from the nursing executives and, as a result, revamped the nursing reorganization so that there would still be nursing leaders at each facility who also provide representation at the network level.

This instance of learning during the FCI implementation could actually have come from anywhere in the creation of a new culture for the system. The FCI team's bypass of nursing administrators is just an example of what can happen before a cultural shift has completely taken hold.

We have to keep an eye continuously on our principles and practices and ask ourselves where we are being inconsistent. What sayings are posted on the walls that we are not honoring in our actions?

Another reminder we gained from this occurrence is the interdependent nature of our actions and other people's responses. The implementation team's decision to exclude a certain group of people was paralleled exactly by that group's failure to ask, "Why aren't we being included?"

The culture recycles itself, mostly unconsciously. We want to ask, "Why wouldn't people in responsible positions speak up for themselves? What stops them from doing so?" But when we acknowledge the systemic logic of people's behavior, we also have to ask, "Who hired the people who are reluctant to speak up? And what was the basis of the hiring decision?"

Do we pursue people who can help us realize our ideal of a diverse team? Or do we look for people just like us? Or do we look for someone who won't rock the boat? Do we recruit people in our institutions who will go along and fit in, and then reserve the right to fault them for not speaking up when it costs us the full use of their talents?

If—as we suspect—fear has been a driving force in the formation of the system's culture, then the transformation of the culture requires us to drive out the fear and find better processes for developing and empowering the people who work in the system.

But we are genuinely puzzled about how to do this. We need everyone to engage in this effort—nurses, physicians, technicians, dietitians, middle managers, secretaries, everyone. It really is not sufficient for just those in system management to try to find a solution. Again, the CQI principle states that the people closest to the process are the ones to be involved in its improvement.

> **W**e cannot leave any key constituencies out of the change process, even when their involvement may make reaching consensus more difficult.

## AN EXAMPLE AT ST. MARYS IN MADISON

Cultural change requires a willingness to shake up the status quo. And that shakeup can be helped or hindered by a hiring decision. At St. Marys Hospital Medical Center in Madison, the then-chief operating officer, Sister Susan Scholl, was faced with the opportunity to bring someone in as vice president of nursing who was an uncharacteristically assertive leader.

Choosing such a person for any executive team is often a leap of faith for the one hiring because of the impact the choice might have on the facility's operations, on other leaders, and employees.

St. Marys has a long history and tradition with its nurses, having had its own nursing school for many years. The tempting route for the COO would have been to select a nursing vice president who would move things along gradually. But instead, she took the risk and hired a vice president who was eager to try a new approach to involve the nurses in issues pertaining to patient care and their own development.

The vice president quickly created a self-governing nursing council whose members serve as the chairs for five or six teams. The teams directly tackle issues pertaining to nursing quality, education, universal standards, nursing services, and so on. The new vice president didn't need to get someone's permission—being hired for the job was the permission. She just took action and provided leadership.

The nurses at Madison are involved in exercising leadership among themselves and within the hospital and handling the issues that are important to them. The nurses on the teams are part of the rank and file who are taking responsibility for the quality of their work and the satisfaction they have in their jobs. In a city where many nurses have voted to join unions, the ones at St. Marys have not.

## THE CASE OF SSMRI

The office of the SSM Rehabilitation Institute (SSMRI) is located at the same site as St. Mary's Health Center—in Richmond Heights, Missouri, a municipality just outside of St. Louis. Most of the staff works out of 13 clinics around the metropolitan area.

The nurses at SSMRI, about one-third of the staff, work in the skilled nursing facility on the second floor of the health center. In 1995 and 1996, they were engaged in the question of whether or not to join a union.

When the vice president of operations, Melinda Clark, took over as president of SSMRI in October 1995, she knew that union interest was a signal of discontent. She set out to learn the source of it.

One of the issues causing dissatisfaction was the difficulty of moving a CQI project through to completion because of the long approval process. The average duration of a CQI team at SSMRI was 18 months, and some teams had been meeting for more than two years without accomplishing noticeable gains. One team, for example, had worked on improving employee rewards and recognition and conducted a satisfaction survey asking for responses to certain employee events. On the survey, more than 90 percent of the employees said they didn't appreciate one of the annual events and asked that it be stopped. The administrators decided to continue having the event anyway, even after a team gathered the data and made a recommendation.

Melinda saw that part of the change needed was to eliminate the attitude of having to ask for permission and replace it with the freedom to take initiative. Within a week of her appointment, the president did away with the CQI team presentations to the administrative council. She let people know that if they identified a project for improvement and it was within the scope of their accountability, they should just go ahead with it. If it was not within their scope, they should request that it be taken on by a group that *could* work on it.

When Melinda told us about SSMRI's constrained environment, we knew that it wasn't a unique situation. At the start of our CQI implementation, we envisioned a new climate in which people would take initiative in improving their jobs; yet, seven years later, the pull of the command-and-control culture was still very much present.

Probably in more cases than we know, projects have wound up "looking like CQI" but, in fact, were products of a culture in which some level of management had dictated—and perhaps even manipulated—a particular finding or result.

One thing Melinda told us that she had discovered early in her search for the source of union organizing was the nurses' unhappiness over an apparent lack of trust and respect. An example came up during a Talk to the President meeting, when a nurse pointed out to her that the nursing policies mandated nurses to work 26 alternating weekends a year, with no substitutions or exceptions allowed. This meant that no nurse could have two consecutive weekends off.

When Melinda told us about this policy, we expressed surprise that anyone even read the nursing policies. In Sister Mary Jean's experience, nursing policies gathered dust as people went about their work. The policies were updated every two or three years for the Joint Commission reviews and then ignored again.

For the two of us, this was another instructive reminder of the deliberate effort that it takes to ferret out the entrenched policies and customs that hinder a new order of management. Beneath the black and white of such policies was an old-line tool for managers and supervisors to use against people who were "difficult." Rather than having face-to-face conversations with individuals about undesirable aspects of their work, a policy infraction could be cited—with apparent objectivity, but with a punitive intent.

## Cultivating a New Climate

The president of SSMRI wanted the staff to be empowered to make independent decisions whenever possible and, at other times, to make cooperative decisions with administrators. The management team would serve as a resource to help people do their jobs, rather than as overseers.

A by-product of the lack of progress by teams at SSMRI was that the term *CQI team* had taken on a negative image. Again, this didn't occur only at SSMRI, but also at other places where teams met for too long and accomplished too little.

Our original belief was that people on teams would set their own goals and move forward as quickly as possible. We wanted the team's mission to say what should be accomplished in a general way, but we did not want to set specific expectations in terms of performance because we thought people could determine that themselves.

We also had a place for "constraints," or the limits in which the team had to work. The constraints, depending on the project, might have been "budget neutral," "no new FTEs," or "capital expenses have to be approved." But some of the constraints put on at the entity level were so restrictive that teams had no authority to do any-thing—a situation that violated the CQI principle that quality is achieved through people.

What we didn't anticipate or understand was that along the way there would be some administrators, managers, and supervisors—intentionally or unintentionally—creating barriers to success rather than facilitating it.

As a result of the unfavorable "CQI" history, the staff at SSMRI changed the name to *deployment teams,* to reflect an action orientation. These teams, following CQI principles, are asked to initiate improvements.

The teams have a framework established up front so that, for example, if a process a team is working on has a capital limitation or an FTE limitation, this is made known at the beginning.

One early deployment team took on the revision of the nursing policies regarding scheduling. The team was given a framework and the goal of coming to a mutual decision between nurses and man-agement that is workable, gives flexibility, and still provides ade-quate staffing. The team designed a new process for scheduling and then educated the entire nursing staff as to how it works.

Deployment teams keep the information on their projects in a book and periodically update the facility's eight-member operations strategy team, which replaced the administrative council.

Once a new deployment team is formed and told the scope and limitations of the project, the facility's leadership team—made up of 90 percent clinical and 10 percent administrative staff—has to indicate unanimous agreement, with a show of hands, that whatever the team creates will be accepted. When this process was first implemented, some leadership team members would just raise their hands and not ask any questions or give any input. But as time has gone on, those with reservations have begun voicing their concerns beforehand—rather than after the fact, as had been the custom.

The operations strategy team's periodic reviews of the project consider whether the team is where it needs to be, if it is on track, and if there is new information the team needs.

## ASSUMING THE RISK OF TRUSTING

Wainwright Industries, a Baldrige Award–winning manufacturing company in Missouri, has served as a mentor to many in the SSM Health Care System. Even though our operations are very different in size and in mission, we have learned some things about building a quality culture from Wainwright's management.

SSMRI's president told us that she took to heart a Wainwright manager's idea of "not always having to drive the bus"—that is, giving decision making to the managers who have the best perspective on what needs to be accomplished. One example was the turning over of hiring decisions to the department heads who have to meet a particular performance target.

In the culture of the entities, control over hiring has tended to be closely held by top management, mostly out of concern that additional personnel would become the proposed solution for every problem.

At SSMRI, the department's financial goal is the performance indicator currently used as the gauge of whether or not a new staff member can be hired. If the department is hitting its goal or going beyond it, the department head can make the decision to add staff for a new program. A group in the department puts together a one-page business plan describing the program and who or what they will need to carry it out.

Decision making within departments encourages risk taking and it also encourages better thinking on the part of the group, Melinda told us. If a department's projected production goes awry for a month or two, people have to devise ways to turn a negative situation around. Going through this process causes people to think through a plan rather than just jump into hiring. Human resources people at SSMRI expected a 20 percent increase in full-time equivalents in the first six months of this new approach, and in fact there was *no* increase.

A process improvement that emerged quickly and inexpensively as a result of this more cooperative and trusting environment at SSMRI is a security system for all 13 clinics. Staff members at one of the clinics were concerned about intruders walking into a sometimes unstaffed reception area while therapists were in treatment rooms. The staff members took it upon themselves to call the 12 other sites to learn if they had a similar issue and what they were doing about it. They found that the newest clinic in St. Charles had simply installed a $27 battery-powered bell that was activated whenever the front door opened. Now, for a total of about $350, all of the clinics have a solution that provides better service to customers and better security for staff.

When we look at the process of this simple improvement, we see that it follows the CQI structure. A team of people noted a problem with a process, gathered data, discovered a best practice, and replicated it.

The question we ask ourselves is, what prevents this kind of process improvement from happening everywhere, all of the time, in our system?

At least a partial answer is something we acknowledged from the beginning of the CQI journey. Continuous improvement is not a "program" to superimpose on top of an existing culture. It has to seep into and transform the culture. The progress that is beginning to be made at SSMRI is coming from a change in the culture—moving from control and mistrust to trust and freedom.

Often managers want to hold financial goals and performance measures as confidential information. Then when a team sets improvement goals for service and quality, the managers discount the team's ideas because the team didn't have all the information it needed to ground the plan in reality. Team projects start to look like useless exercises instead of real problem-solving activities.

When leaders share the bottom-line numbers, goals, and measures, groups of employees can actually work together to produce the results on which everyone is aligned.

Further, when staff members have these numbers and are fully informed of the progress or setbacks in their performance, they are empowered to work on solutions or further improvements. In the climate of trust and initiative being created at SSMRI, for example, every new program or process implemented by a department group is evaluated for its effectiveness. If it is not effective, the people who oversee the program—not the president—are accountable for developing an action plan to turn it around. The president gets a report about the problem and what steps are being taken by whom to correct the situation in a set period of time. If the improvement doesn't occur, the entire leadership team is asked to look together at what changes occurred that could have caused the downward trend or what new processes were put in place that weren't evaluated for their impact on performance.

In this kind of environment, the executive leader can serve as a teacher or coach—that is, not the problem solver, but someone who can contribute knowledge and experience as needed to those who are working on the problem. Instead of seeking permission, the staff seeks more information, background, and explanations. SSMRI's president told us that she often sees herself as a sort of technical advisor—answering questions, but always turning the decision back to the person accountable.

Between April and July 1996, SSMRI deployed five teams working on major improvement initiatives, including the changes in scheduling policy. In addition, the president and the seven members of the operations strategy team have undergone 360-degree performance evaluations by people who work with them and plan to have four such evaluations each year. Everyone on the leadership team was scheduled to begin undergoing those evaluations by the end of 1996.

As a result of the work being done to create a new climate at SSMRI, the nurses voted against joining a union in July 1996 by a vote of 38 to 31.

*Just as hospitals could not turn back changes in reimbursement, nurses cannot return to the idealized time of bedside care. Nurses are at the line of demarcation. They have to choose to take on a higher level of responsibility or risk losing their professional status.*

7

# INTEGRATING CLINICAL AND FUNCTIONAL SERVICES WITH CQI

*The shift to integrated networks in health care is a competitive and economic need in populous areas. Bringing CQI to the process of integration also helps to serve our customers' needs.*

A brief document, entitled "Statement of Future Reality 2000," was one of the driving factors in the formation of the St. Louis Health Care Network (SLHCN) in 1994. The statement declares the system's commitment to the health status of the entire community in partnership with other social structures, and it shifts our emphasis from acute care to holistic health.

This document broadened the scope of the SSM Health Care System's mission and reinforced our determination to remain a viable presence in the marketplace. In the decade that preceded the SLHCN's formation, we learned that no matter how well intentioned a health care institution may be, it can only endure when its structures and practices are aligned to provide quality care *and* to contain costs.

It was also clear to us, after the most apparent cost-saving measures had been taken within the system, that a more comprehensive strategy was needed to deploy all of our resources—human, financial, and material—in the most effective way.

We believe that participating in integrated delivery networks provides a structure for improving care while lowering costs. Consequently, SSM Health Care System facilities in Oklahoma and Wisconsin, as well as St. Louis, have formed such networks.

## THE ST. LOUIS HEALTH CARE NETWORK

With the creation of the St. Louis Health Care Network, we brought under one umbrella the resources and abilities of 8000 people (including 3600 physicians), seven health care facilities, six affiliates, and hundreds of programs and services.

The health care facilities in the network, all in Missouri, are St. Mary's Health Center in Richmond Heights, St. Joseph's Health Center in St. Charles, St. Joseph Hospital West in Lake St. Louis, St. Joseph's Hospital in Kirkwood, Cardinal Glennon Children's Hospital in St. Louis, SSM Rehabilitation Institute in Richmond Heights, and DePaul Health Center in Bridgeton. DePaul was the only one of these entities that was not then part of the system, but was later purchased from the Daughters of Charity of St. Vincent DePaul.

SLHCN's executives called on the principles and tools of CQI to bring themselves together as a team and identify their objectives. The first overall goal was to create a delivery system across the St. Louis metropolitan area that provides excellent value and service while achieving a $30 million to $40 million reduction in the cost of operations. The approach to this goal was the integration of several functional and clinical services within the network.

## THE SCOPE OF FCI

The functional and clinical integration effort (referred to as *FCI*) began in April 1995, with the creation of a steering team of about 14 people, including two SLHCN vice presidents to serve as coleaders of the team, some of the system's central region leaders, and the facility presidents.

Ron Levy, a vice president of SLHCN and coleader of FCI, told us that when the group first gathered, CQI provided a jump start for its work. The common experience of working on CQI teams and using its tools and processes eliminated the need to spend time figuring out how to work together. The team could move right into gathering baseline data and creating a mission and objectives.

One fear that the planning team had at the outset was that, based on earlier experience, using the CQI seven-step model to help move the FCI project would take too long. SLHCN's leaders had given themselves just six months to establish the plan and begin implementing the functional and clinical integration. The team, challenged to focus quickly on accomplishing complex redesigns, found ways to use the principles, model, and tools without being overly concerned about "dotting every i" of the seven-step process.

Bob Henkel, the other coleader of FCI and a newcomer to the system from DePaul, said that he viewed the use of CQI's principles and tools by the steering team as the first major test of CQI methods. Up until FCI, Bob said his perception was that CQI teams had been employed on relatively small, localized issues that didn't receive much attention. When the steering team began relying on CQI as a foundational structure for moving through a large process in a tight time frame, the members developed a better appreciation for its value.

The CQI methodology required the teams to have some baseline data before any changes were designed or implemented. Both numerical and qualitative data were the foundation for the discussions that took place. This, Henkel said, ensured that the the teams were relying on facts rather than on emotions, opinions, or hunches.

We have discovered in organizations we work with—not just our own—that while decision making by objective data may be regarded as a common discipline, it isn't always applied. The tendency to go on gut feeling or strongly held opinions is always ready to come into play when there are no ground rules for using a more rigorous methodology.

Bob said he found the discipline of CQI immensely helpful not only in implementation, but also in monitoring the progress and in going back to make corrections and find out why certain things happened or did not happen.

## CULTURE PRINT SURVEY

One of the first things the team did, in May 1995, was to conduct a "culture print" survey, using a statistically significant sample of about 1000 individuals from across the network—physicians, administrators, and employees in all areas.

The steering team recognized that the cultural aspects of the change that facilities would undergo would be as important as the technical aspects. The object of the culture print was to learn the attitudes within the organization and see what preparation was needed to effect the changes successfully. Two of the hospitals— DePaul and St. Joseph's in Kirkwood—were new to the system and had operated within completely different cultures. Even those that were veterans of the system had their own local cultures. The team wanted to know what barriers existed in order to make the most compelling case for change.

The culture print revealed some common attitudes across the network. One consistent view was that the organization was hierarchical, pushing ideas from the top down. There also was a sense that process took precedence over action. Another significant attitude was a lack of trust, at least some of which resulted from breakdowns in communication as information is dispersed through channels. Fear was also notable in the organization, partly as result of the lack of trust and partly from a sense of impending change.

On the positive side, the culture print revealed a belief in the organization's strong values. The survey revealed, too, that people at all levels felt there was an institutional commitment to quality.

As part of the response to what was learned in the culture print, a communications plan was developed to lay out the FCI project every step of the way and to get feedback from people. Town hall meetings and hot lines were set up. Q&A bulletins on specific issues were published. Presidents of the facilities received "talking points" and scripts to use in meetings with their employees.

Another response to the culture print data was to fill the FCI planning teams with more frontline employees than with management staff. This was to lessen the perception of a hierarchy dictating change, as well as to demonstrate the commitment to have employees involved in decision making. Balancing the team in this way, while it had advantages, impeded decisive action during implementation and also gave rise to some misunderstanding among managers.

## THE FCI TEAM

Between 120 to 150 people were selected to serve on the teams to design and develop the models for functional and clinical integration. Representatives where chosen from the different organizations so that when smaller teams were formed, there would be specific skills from various levels and departments in each of the network facilities, including some physicians.

Team members had to commit 20 hours a week for six months. The investment of time signaled the seriousness of the project. They would work in teams of 8 to 10 people, creating the plan for integrating their clinical or functional area across the network, communicating that plan back to the entities, and engaging the facilities in implementation.

Most of the participants already were grounded in the CQI principles and knew the steps for gathering and analyzing data and redefining or redesigning systems and processes. Many already had had practical experience working on CQI teams. Just to make sure that everyone could speak the same language, the FCI teams went through a basic CQI review and a refresher on terminology. Consultants from Deloitte Touche, who were assisting with national benchmarking, also participated in some of the training so that they would be familiar with the specific CQI tools and processes used.

Most of the first track of the project, spanning May, June, and July 1995, was spent identifying the opportunities for integration. The team selected the following 11 areas for integration across the network.

1. Hotel services, including housekeeping, dietary, maintenance, and laundry

2. Ancillary management, including care pathway and protocol development

3. Case management

4. Surgery

5. Laboratories

6. Finance

7. Materiel management

8. Women's services

9. Heart services

10. Patient care delivery—patient care model

11. Patient care delivery—documentation

Nine of the 11 teams would benchmark, both internally and nationally, the best practices for improved quality, service, and cost-effectiveness. For the women's services and heart services teams no financial goals were set. Instead, the teams would look for a more strategic approach to offering those two major services across the metropolitan area, instead of hospital by hospital.

## SOME ISSUES OF INTEGRATION

We doubt if any organization ever gets to undertake major change in an ideal way. The constraints of time, budgets, and marketplace competition, plus accountability for continuing to provide the products and services of the organization, all infringe on the ideal plan for change.

In the SLHCN, time and budget considerations definitely influenced the steering team's decision to develop the integration models and start up the FCI implementation within six months.

### The Time Frame

The network was seeking a change of great magnitude in a short span of time. Some of the consulting firms that received SLHCN's request for a proposal cautioned that few, if any, organizations had integrated seven hospitals at one time. With seven hospitals working on 11 areas of integration, SLHCN was actually taking on 77 projects.

Consultants also told the network executives that achieving the cultural change that integration called for would take 12 to 18 months of preparation. Ideally, they said, an organization would use the discoveries from the culture print to plan a year's worth of communications and education to embed the idea of a network and convey the commitment to employee involvement. Only then should actual change begin. Within the time frame already set, however, taking that much time to lay groundwork was not possible.

Perhaps because the FCI implementation began so soon after its initiation, the process has gone more slowly than the steering team had envisioned. But there are other causes as well.

Even though a team of 120 seems large, it represented less than 2 percent of the network's employee population. To gather any momentum, the implementation process needed to draw many more people from each hospital into the effort. Such an enrollment effort takes time.

## Leverage Points

Another reason we suspect for delays in moving from the teams' models to reality was a lack of sufficient leverage within the organizations. The team members, who by design were more often coworkers than managers, had the challenging job of returning to their respective institutions to educate hundreds of people in a new way of thinking about their work without the benefit of an official title or a ready-made constituency.

There is a paradox here in that the teams' composition was a response to concerns about a hierarchy-driven organization. Yet key leaders have to be on board to drive the change in their organizations.

Ron Levy said he was one of those most adamant that the teams not be loaded with managers. But he told us that if he had it to do again, he would involve more managers if for no other reason than to gain their knowledge of the institutional leverage points. One difficulty with this, of course, is that people in positions of leadership in a hospital can easily be taken away from meetings by critical or emergency circumstances. Asking for half of the leader's work time for a six-month period is usually viewed as too much.

Ron believed that the implementation probably would have gone more smoothly if each institution also had had an internal team at the beginning. Members of the implementation team could have returned periodically to their institutions, shared information, and gathered feedback from team members inside. In this way, there would have been a larger core of ownership. More people would have had information about the changes and why they were needed. Accurate reports would have been cascading through the facilities over the six months of planning.

This structure would have kept people's attention on the process of FCI over time, rather than having a small group come in and lay it all out at once. We found that a natural resistance tends to arise when employees or managers feel they are only brought in at the very end. Even some people whom the steering team believed had been briefed on the progress of the FCI said things like, "I didn't know anything about this, and I don't think this is going to work here."

## Physician Involvement

One of the biggest issues to deal with was the size of the medical staff in the network—about 3600—and the lack of front-end participation by physicians. Some of the gains in patient care that eventually will be realized have been delayed because of insufficient physician involvement.

Bob Henkel told us that by virtue of the way physicians ordinarily practice in hospitals, it wasn't in their culture to carry the message of integration back to lounges, lunchrooms, and ORs. He said if he could do it over again, he would involve the physicians in a different way.

Even though physicians on the documentation team spent hours explaining the system to their colleagues, there was an outcry about the new patient documentation form on the day it was implemented.

When the resistance occurred, Ron and Bob began working with the elected presidents of the medical staffs so that they had a detailed understanding of all of the projects being worked on. In that way, the presidents became willing to champion the documentation sytem with every medical executive committee and get the model approved. These elected presidents in many cases are not part of the employed medical groups in the network, but they became allies once they were brought into the process.

With patient care delivery, the FCI team used the concepts of national benchmarking and replication. Their idea was that piloting and replicating successful work would eliminate the need for every location to try out its own methods. But when the team tried to put the model into action, it didn't succeed. Because they weren't involved in the process, many physicians responded by saying, "That won't work here."

The feedback physicians eventually provided was used to alter the patient care model. Having it six months earlier would have saved both time and money.

*For clinical integration to be effective, the medical staff has to be involved in designing change because they are such key stakeholders in the delivery system.*

# MORE ON NURSING

As we wrote in chapter 6, the FCI planning team had to go back to the drawing board with the model for nursing reorganization, partly as a result of leaving the vice presidents of nursing off the planning team.

Bob Henkel said that at first he believed the top nurses' involvement in their hospitals' administrative councils would keep them sufficiently in the information loop to feel informed, even though they were not on the planning team. He learned only much later how disengaged the nurses felt from the process.

The model designed by the team eliminated the position of vice president of nursing at the individual hospitals and created a vice president of nursing for the network. The thinking behind the plan was that with a common delivery system and common standards and practices, one executive would be sufficient. It would also elevate nursing to a top network position for the first time.

When it came time to implement the new patient care model, the vice presidents of nursing, rather than championing the change, took a hands-off attitude because they had not been involved in the process. Thus, there was no support from senior nurses, on a day-by-day basis, for the patient care system that was being implemented.

Feedback on the nursing reorganization from nursing executives within the system caused the team to take another look. The central region nurse executives, plus the nursing vice presidents and Bob Henkel, used CQI methodology to create a new organization plan that keeps the local nursing vice presidents in place. All of these VPs form a nursing council of chief nurse executives. A chair, elected by the council members, works directly with the network's management team. The council has responsibility for the implementation of the basic care delivery model, and each of the vice presidents has a networkwide responsibility.

## Entity Presidents

With the entity presidents participating on the planning team, the goal not only was to have their input but also to have them disseminate FCI information to medical staffs, management teams, and employees. But sometimes the communication was haphazard and inconsistent, rather than orchestrated.

We learned from SLHCN executives that some presidents, while on the steering team, were not all really on the team. That is, they had not bought into the idea of functional and clinical integration in a way that could have them communicate it powerfully. They were not as prepared as we thought for what the FCI implementation would mean in terms of change, what it would mean in practice, and what the consequences would be.

Understanding change intellectually and grasping it viscerally are extremely different phenomena. Whenever we mistake the first for the second, we are bound to be disappointed with the outcome.

One facet of integration that can be difficult for leaders to accept is that some control and autonomy at the local level is lessened. The separate identity of the individual health facility is blurred by membership in a network. When this integration is still new, we found, presidents face the dilemma of taking on ownership in the network while still being held responsible for the operations, expenses, volume, and so on of their local hospital. Their question could be, "If I take this action for the network, will it be at the expense of my own institution?"—or vice versa.

There was also the issue of presidents thinking that the network only added another layer of bureaucracy and busywork, and that what they needed was be left alone to run their hospital. As someone faced with bringing the FCI venture together, Ron told us candidly how he sometimes wanted to say to various presidents, "Either get on board or get out early." For him it was not a matter of disparaging individuals or their abilities, but rather letting them know that a network, by its nature, can't accommodate leaders with a Lone Ranger style of leading. Several consultants advised the executives of SLHCN to determine quickly who was on board and who was not.

Just as with the initial work of CQI, independent health care professionals don't arrive naturally at the idea of integrated systems across hospitals. It is something that requires massive education, exposure, and evolution.

Our expectations about middle managers being empowered to be part of important changes were once again unfulfilled because some of those at the top level of the entities weren't sufficiently communicating the depth and scope of the integration process.

When directors were not informed continuously about impending changes in their department, they felt disengaged—especially if an employee from their department was on the team attempting to implement the change.

Even though the CQI principles emphasize that the people doing the work are the ones to make the process changes, supervisors and managers were still ingrained with the idea that they were the decision makers and the directors. Now, FCI was asking middle managers even more emphatically to undergo a fundamental shift in their thinking and behavior.

# TAKING OWNERSHIP

The key difference between the network executives and the entity presidents regarding FCI is not that one group is smarter or better. The difference, rather, is the depth of ownership and the degree of participation. Those who became immersed in the implementation—no matter what their level—had the experience of being engaged in a larger possibility, while those who stayed apart from the project saw their involvement simply as one more task to be done.

Ron told us that he found himself reaching "different plateaus of understanding." Over time, the more individuals are exposed to and engaged in learning about the concepts of integration, the more they buy in to it. But it seemed—just as with CQI—that being able to effectively communicate about FCI came not from the understanding of concepts, but from a profound ownership of the goal. This happened at different times for different people.

Bob Henkel told us that at the beginning, some team members insisted that FCI wouldn't work and that it would be a "here today, gone tomorrow" kind of thing. As he observed the teams in action, sitting in on many meetings, he saw the naysayers of August and September become zealots for the project by January and February. Some transformed from being the ones dragged into action to being the ones pushing to move faster.

The ownership of FCI seemed to happen more successfully once individuals—including the entity presidents—took on responsibility for an area, rather than simply being informed about what was supposed to happen. When people accept accountability across an entire network, it ignites their interest, learning, and understanding.

As we had seen before in the system, there was a sort of parochialism and a lack of desire to replicate what others had done, no matter how successful. During the FCI process, however, there has been some breaking down of those barriers. Some FCI teams became passionate about the idea of working inside a network instead of for one hospital. They began to see the vision of being part of the St. Louis Health Care Network, which led them away from the narrowness of a single entity and toward greater appreciation for the processes of benchmarking and replicating best practices.

## IMPROVEMENTS IN SIGHT

We are realizing that some of our expectations about how fast change occurs have to be let go. Organizational change evolves over long periods. Some of the results we thought we might see in six months have actually taken a year or two. Changes that we wanted to happen in two years are happening in five or six years. We still would say that, by and large, people are not comfortable with replicating other institutions' processes—but they are becoming *more* comfortable than they were five years ago.

> **A**ttempts at cultural transformation aren't failures just because it takes longer than expected to see results.

FCI is not being effected as quickly as the steering team had planned, yet change is happening and barriers are falling. People are now cross-pollinating ideas and learning from each other.

By late 1996, the patient care delivery model and the patient care documentation model were both being implemented in all of the SLHCN facilities. As more employees become engaged with these key integrations, the more ownership is evident. Nurses, for example, are owning the new patient care delivery model and, as a result, experience a much greater stake in the concept of FCI than they had at the beginning.

As Bob Henkel continued to oversee the progress of the implementation, he told us that the patient care delivery model started to demonstrate its potential capacity to improve service and cost at the most important point—the patient bedside.

In addition, the patient care delivery documentation system is operating across the network. Every hospital now uses the same form for collecting clinical data so that, as information accumulates, the network will have comparative data on the quality of care.

With the first round of FCI, the baseline data is being gathered. Then the task will be to look at the information and see what can be done to improve the processes. The CQI tools will be in place, Bob said, but it will take discipline to use them.

As information is stored in this uniform system, the network will also have a greater capacity for transmitting patient records to the site at which they are needed.

It becomes easier to move personnel from site to site as needed when there are common organizational structures, processes, and systems for patient care.

Surgical directors are meeting together on an ongoing basis, and they are using a conceptual model for change as a road map. An example of internal benchmarking success was a surgical team that discovered the same vendor charging three different prices for the same implants and orthotics within SLHCN. It is a basic finding, yet it gives evidence of the value of examining what others are doing for possible replication.

Hotel services areas recently signed a contract across the entire network that will save $3 million.

The concept of integration is giving a whole new perspective to the areas of women's services and heart services. Those teams are looking from a metropolitan viewpoint, rather than a hospital viewpoint.

Each of the 11 teams is following a road map and, when necessary, taking minor detours. They are all, in varying degrees, seeing positive movements in their areas. On a day-to-day basis, much of the work done by the teams is being lived out. There are successes, even though they may look different from what was originally expected.

## MATERIEL MANAGEMENT

One of the best examples of success with FCI so far has been the work of the materiel management team. The project was to centralize the network's purchasing function under one roof. Receiving, storeroom, central supply, and mail distribution would all stay in their respective locations.

Centralized purchasing streamlines the management function and brings together the work of five employee groups that had been responsible for supplying eight facilities, including the small Arcadia Valley Hospital in Pilot Knob, Missouri.

Before the creation of SLHCN, each of the five purchasing entities had its own materiel management director. In the new structure, the plan created one director of purchasing and one director of operations, both reporting to a network vice president of materiel management, Tony Trupiano.

Even though the 130 employees affected by the redesign of purchasing is a smaller number than those in other areas, the scope of the project in terms of supplies and supply dollars is large. Access to supplies affects virtually every department, and the annual budget is $75 million.

The 10-member design team was composed of customers from nursing services and surgical services; staff members from purchasing, receiving, and supply distribution; a storeroom manager; and two directors. The mix of employees and managers followed the CQI principle of involving the people most responsible for the process. This team, working with consultants, used CQI data gathering and analysis tools to design a centralized purchasing process, as well as a process for implementing the design.

Because every facility had its own methods, the team had to standardize processes such as moving documents from receiving to purchasing to accounts payable. The team also developed two standard requisition processes, one for facilities on the electronic network and one for those still on a paper system. As facilities convert all of their functions to the system's information network, they will switch to electronic requisitioning.

Although the conceptual design was good, Tony felt the real key was holding several preimplementation meetings at each of the entities. The director of purchasing met with primary customers from surgery, pharmacy, laboratory, and nursing five or six times between February and early July, prior to the consolidation at one site. Other groups with a stake in supply availability were also invited. The meetings allowed customers to raise questions and concerns about centralized purchasing upfront and have them addressed by someone who knew the answers.

Some customers had concerns about giving up the security of having a purchasing office on site. If they needed a supply on an emergency basis, they could run down and have it taken care of. Their fear was having to deal with a purchasing office across town that wouldn't be able to meet those needs. As a result, the team developed a process for emergency orders.

After the move on July 8, postimplementation meetings have been conducted at the hospitals to find out from customers about any outstanding issues that need resolution. So far, Tony said, problems have been minimal.

The materiel management team began to implement the new employee structure in late January and early February 1996. It was difficult, Tony told us, because people were naturally fearful. They didn't know at first if they would lose their jobs or what new job they would have to take on. Most were unfamiliar with the new purchasing site, DePaul Health Center, which was chosen because of the available space.

People on the team worked individually with the employees to ease their fears, explain what had to be accomplished with the centralization, inform them about the job posting process, and keep them involved. Fortunately, staff reductions were able to be made through attrition, so no one was left without a job. That increased people's comfort level with the changes.

Purchasing directors, for example, aware that they were going to be redeployed in the network, continued to operate their individual purchasing offices until July. Some of the directors then went to work in the system's health businesses operating at the corporate office.

Employees who were scheduled to move to the location at DePaul Health Center went to the site and were involved in the layout of office space. They had the opportunity to gradually get used to the idea that in July they would no longer be purchasing many things for one hospital, but would become a product line specialist for eight health care facilities.

Tony said the result of those seven months of preliminary work was that purchasing employees from the five different hospitals came together as a team very quickly at DePaul Health Center. As they helped one another with questions and went to lunch together, Tony said that the separate hospital identities and cultures disappeared.

The vice president of materiel management cleared his calendar for the week of July 8, expecting to be putting out fires with the new purchasing process. Instead, he told us that it was probably the most peaceful week he has had in that position.

The main improvement the materiel management team would have made, Tony said, was speeding up information to employees so as to reduce their stress and ease fears.

This was the first centralization process the network implemented, and it was the first time that human resources had to deal with how to communicate such a process. Other centralizations that have followed, with larger groups of employees, have had an easier time rolling out the process.

The model for the reorganization of materiel management has saved money and improved the purchasing and distribution processes across the network. Success surely was eased by the number of people involved. The smaller the organization, the easier it is to gain peoples' trust and engage them in change more quickly. But another part of this success was the clarity of the model and the determination of the team to implement the change effectively. Change is almost always met by resistance of some sort. But that resistance was overcome.

As resistance lessens, change does start to happen. There are now 200 to 300 people in the network facilities who really do grasp what FCI is all about and are pulling for it. The work of implementing FCI continues, with some of the conceptual models needing to be redesigned as they are applied.

By the end of 1996, FCI had moved into phase III—from project status to part of the normal course of the organization. It still needs to be adjusted from time to time. But what is most needed now is a model for keeping attention on it so that the progress made isn't lost.

*A model for major change based on quality principles helps the complex integration of functional and clinical processes work to the benefit of managers, employees, and patients.*

C H A P T E R    **8**

# MEASURING FOR QUALITY'S SAKE

*Objective measurement is the main tool our institution uses to determine if we are accomplishing what we say we are committed to. Statistics that measure the quality of our processes will eventually come to be as accepted in our system as expense reports are today.*

.........................................

One of the five CQI principles we adopted in 1990 was decision making by objective data. This is one of those principles that everyone can agree with in theory, but has a harder time putting into action.

Before CQI, the customary and required measures for health care institutions were all in place: income, expenses, indebtedness, beds, occupancy rates, lengths of stay, the ratio of Medicare/ Medicaid patients to privately insured, charity cases, and so on. Those numbers gave us a window to a certain reality that, although important, did not illuminate root causes or give access to improvements in quality.

Peter Senge, in his book *The Fifth Discipline,* writes about the difficulty of managing quality in a service business because of the intangibility of the activities. He says,

> *Because service quality is intangible, there is a strong tendency to manage service businesses by focusing on what is most tangible: such as numbers of customers served, costs of providing the service, and revenues generated. But focusing on what's easily measured leads to "looking good without being good," to having measurable performance indicators that are acceptable, yet not providing quality service.*[1]

## THE EXISTING CULTURE

Much of what has been measured in health care is the easy and obvious, having little or no bearing on our customers' expectations or satisfaction. As far back as 15 or so years ago, patients and other customers began letting it be known that they did not agree with our measures of performance. And it has taken those of us in health care a few more years, with the spur of competition, to understand that the people we wanted to serve could indeed find other places to turn.

Managing for quality in health care requires that we now measure not only how long we are keeping our patients, but also how well we are satisfying them. Our opinions about the quality of our care can now be validated or disproved by data gathered from the recipients of that care.

In the first phase of our CQI implementation, quality teams learned to obtain baseline data on existing processes or procedures by itemizing elements of the activity—steps, minutes, hand-offs, reworks, and so on. By tracking and plotting those numbers, we learned to determine when processes are in statistical control, where there are variations, and whether the variations are common or special. The team could then design a new process or redesign an existing process accordingly.

In the second phase of CQI, we incorporated many different kinds of employee surveys, patient satisfaction surveys, and market surveys as elements of long-range strategic and financial planning.

Even as people have become adept at measuring for process improvements and for planning, however, measurement as a tool for improving our everyday performance still has not become an integral part of the culture. Of course, financial outcomes are measured and monitored regularly. But there has been no comparable set of quality or performance measures.

In building a culture of quality supported by measurement, a way to learn how well we are doing is to notice where our focus is. Are we still looking inward to our opinions, our mental models, and our educated guesses? Or are we looking outward to results, outcomes, and feedback from the people we are serving?

We have no shortage of patients and other customers who will reflect back to us how well we do our jobs—if we ask them. We have basic questions we can use to determine our effectiveness: How well are people doing? What are people saying about us? How is the whole community doing?

Those simple questions can be asked by every single person employed within the SSM Health Care System because we all have customers—either internal, external, or both.

The head of a hospital department, for example, can ask, "How well are people doing?" To respond would first require that the department head identify all of the people within the area—individual employees, patients, and other customers to whom a service is provided. Then the requirements and expectations for each of those groups would need to be known; a measuring device to gauge the outcomes against the requirements and expectations would have to be created; and, finally, the leverage points for making the biggest difference would have to be found.

## FEAR OF FAILURE

One reason for the slowness to grasp the value of this kind of measurement is that in the past, various scores and ratings were so personalized that people had little experience of value or learning. From the time we all went to first grade, a score on a test wasn't a measure of the performance of the teacher or a way to measure progress. It was the way we were personally evaluated.

People go through 12 or 16 or 18 years of measurement that evaluates how good they are. Human beings don't like the judgment to come down on the side of "not good." So most of us determine a level of performance that will gain a passing grade and keep us within an acceptable range.

Clearly there are many people in every field who are willing to stretch further and take the risk of failing. But we have noticed in our institutions (and we don't believe they are unique) that, for the most part, people are not ambitious to make breakthrough improvements in themselves, their processes, or their work environments.

Even for some who do have that ambition, the joy of learning and joy of improving is driven out of them by the systems in which they work. Supervisors may say things like the following:

- "Don't come to me with something that will take more time or work."

- "Let's not rock the boat."

- "It might make the boss look bad."

- "If we try for something better and don't make it, we're going to get hammered."

Every organization has its unspoken, unwritten culture—like something in the air that cannot be defined or even described. In the presence of high-technology medical equipment, telecommunications, and information systems, it may be difficult for some to understand. But the SSM Health Care System operates within a culture that has remnants lingering from more than 100 years ago. Authority, hierarchy, and fear made up parts of that inherited culture. Employees who became supervisors instilled in others the fear they felt.

This fact does not give cause for blame, any more than one would blame someone for starting to speak the language or eat the food of the country to which they moved. As long as the fear of standing out or speaking up has gone unacknowledged, it hovers like an invisible hand and no action can be taken against it.

In traditional management theory, measurement was used to assess an individual. People were reluctant to set a specific goal, because if the goal wasn't achieved it would mean *they* had failed. Numerical assessments were something to avoid, evade, ignore, or hide because they often were associated with getting in trouble with the boss. Some employees probably still suspect that measurements will be used by senior management or supervisors as a club.

If a person wants to improve something, that means changing it. And if you change something that draws attention to yourself, you get singled out. It could be by a physician, another department, or your own boss. People ask, "Why draw attention to myself? If it doesn't work, I'll get complaints. If it does work, it still requires change." So the solution is to avoid the aggravation. Keep everyone happy by maintaining the status quo. Thus, the processes people learned and unquestioningly took on are perpetuated and passed down to the next round of managers.

Some middle managers have been at their jobs 10, 15, or 20 years and doing them in a routine, repetitive way. The idea that it could be done differently is interpreted by them as an indictment of their performance to date. Higher levels of leaders haven't succeeded in conveying that performance measurement is not about people, but about processes.

## SOME MISSING ELEMENTS

Measurement as a diagnostic tool for checking the effectiveness of a plan or a process and determining the points of leverage has not yet become the way of thinking among the majority of managers or employees. Thus, the effort to build a culture in which measurement is an everyday tool for improvement doesn't begin in a cleared field. We have to first uproot the idea that measurement is personal evaluation.

We developed two courses three or four years ago to address some of these issues, and they are still available. One is a three-day facilitator training for administrative council members. In it, we tried to expand and deepen the skills of those at the vice president level and above in using measurement. One of the teachings was how to use measurement as a process with other individuals. The second course, also three days long, is called CQI for Managers. This one deals with the use of the measuring process in coaching.

Something lacking, though, is that we have not developed another set of courses to continue to reinforce these courses. Some new courses work on personal skills for the manager, but they do not follow up on using measurement in an empowering way.

Another thing we have observed is that we are not, in the system or in particular entities, managing to the measure. Entities may decide that a particular measure is important and do a patient survey to collect the data. The data may be put in a report and sent around the organization. But if we go back into the facilities, chances are better than likely that we will not find anything being done to impact that particular measure. We have not found people saying, "The response for our ER admitting process is unacceptable, and we are going to make a real effort to make that better and achieve this level of improvement by this date."

We have asked, "What actions were taken after that survey data was collected?" And, instead of hearing about actions, we hear reasons and justifications for low ER scores.

What is missing is the principle, "Patients are our first priority." Instead, too often bosses seem to be the first priority and patients are second. Instead of finding out what patients need, too often we work to obtain what we need: name, phone number, medical history, insurance information, and so on.

Another example of not managing to a measure has been that over the past three or four years, job stress and insecurity have been measured as a top concern of system employees across the board. Yet we have not heard of a quality improvement team at any entity working on the project of decreasing the level of employee stress.

When survey data showed that employees had a feeling that quality in their institutions had slipped, we did not see entity teams forming to check out the reality of that concern, discover its source, and see where improvements could be made.

Employee surveys and the FCI culture print survey have shown that fear is present in the workplace. Yet facilities aren't specifically working to alleviate that fear.

We have yet to see an entire organization align on activities that would impact an important institutionwide issue and then make significant headway on that issue.

Some progress was made in this respect with the St. Louis Health Care Network's 1995 strategic financial plan. The leaders of the network, in developing the overall plan, had used the report card on quality and patient satisfaction from the St. Louis Healthcare Alliance to identify a strategic focus in patient satisfaction. The alliance, described in chapter 4, had established about eight clinical areas and several quality indicators for each area to measure the performance of hospitals throughout the metropolitan area.

The first plan submitted by SLHCN revealed a huge disconnect between what had been determined to be important objectives for the network and what each individual hospital in the network was doing. When this was pointed out, the planners took the proposal back to do additional work, both in the financial and strategic aspects.

When the plan was resubmitted, we could see that individual hospitals had taken the networkwide concerns and initiatives and begun to focus their plans on those specific areas. This demonstrated the first step of an organization's creating its strategic plan to impact an objective measurement, and then having individual facilities align with that plan.

The next step will be to determine how well the individual facilities' projects were designed, with respect to their particular resources and capacities, to favorably impact the most pertinent patient satisfaction measurement. For instance, a hospital that customers in surveys rated "worse than expected" in one of its core clinical areas would be expected to have at least one specific plan to improve that area.

If measurement were being used as a tool for improvement, hospital staffs could be seen putting their plan into into action, checking its performance after three months or so of operation to see if the strategy is panning out or not, and then making adjustments. This is the PDCA cycle that is at the heart of improving processes.

But this won't happen if people feel they have to deny the reality of the numbers—or at least not call attention to them—so as to protect their jobs or their reputations. This condition may be why, in most organizations, people revert to opinions and hunches rather than objective data to make decisions. A major breakthrough in a quality culture is learning to separate oneself from the numbers that measure what we are doing or have done.

Soon, the corporate office will have a mechanism for getting feedback from the facilities on how well our operations are doing compared to the needs and expectations of those in the field.

Staff in the Quality Resource Center have designed an evaluation form to be sent out on a monthly basis beginning in 1997. We will be able to see how our functional areas are perceived and use the data to determine what projects should be undertaken to improve the processes in those areas.

We envision that staff in the corporate office will have to overcome our own tendency to take evaluation personally. It will be good practice for us, and it will model for others the willingness to respond to measurement as a tool for improving.

## A CHANGE IN QUALITY ASSURANCE

In 1995, we became convinced that the system had to put more attention on measurements, not less. If we had really been attuned to the implications of our systemwide lack of measurement, we might have turned our attention there earlier.

Two or three years ago we were still receiving quality assurance (QA) reports from the entities that consistently referred to a 95 percent compliance with the requirement threshold. "No further action required" would be the stock statement on page after page listing hundreds of items being measured, all at the 95 percent level.

This type of measurement, unlike the measurement advocated in CQI, became a sort of security blanket. The sense of a quest for excellence was not present. People would say, "This is good enough." Instead of being spurred to find ways to improve, departments would find comfort in performing at the national norm. If hospitals nationwide had a 0 percent to 4 percent infection rate, and a hospital's infection rate was measured at 0.4, the tendency would be to say, "We're as good as everybody else."

In building a quality culture, however, being as good as everybody else is not the point. Being satisfied with even 99 percent is not a characteristic of a quality environment.

Part of the education of the system management team was to realize that CQI would never be present as "the way we work here" if the status quo was left on the table as an option. Now we could see that this had to be part of everyone else's educational process.

When we continued to get all favorable QA reports on hospital departments, we said, "Good. We're glad you are measuring all these things and that you are performing at this level. Now what are you working to improve?" The response we heard was that nothing was being worked on, because everything was okay.

As a result, we changed our own requirements for reporting. We acknowledged that part of QA's job was to monitor functions of the health care institution for regulatory purposes. And we said it is not acceptable to say we don't have to do anything just because the facility is performing at acceptable levels.

We changed the forms being used and asked the QA people to report on specific places they could see to improve, what steps would be taken, and how progress would be measured. We asked them to report on progress on a quarterly basis. We said that if the action plan doesn't produce the result, that's okay, but then what else will you try?

The QA professionals themselves began to catch on to this different emphasis. In the departments, though, there were still managers who did not want to have to initiate an improvement project if everything met the requirement threshold. What should have been an integral part of their jobs—improving the quality of their processes—was occurring for them like just another project. It is a difficult mind-set to break through.

# MALCOLM BALDRIGE NATIONAL QUALITY AWARD CRITERIA

As a way to accelerate the process of system entities' integrating measurement into our daily decision making, we turned to a valuable structure that many U.S. organizations have begun to use: the Baldrige Award criteria.

Until the mid 1990s, the prestigious Malcolm Baldrige National Quality Award process, named after the former U.S. Secretary of Commerce, was only open to for-profit companies. Over time, many states adapted the Baldrige Award criteria and self-evaluation process as the pattern for statewide quality awards for local companies. Then, in 1995, the Baldrige Award committee distributed the health care pilot criteria, specifically for health care institutions.

At the leadership conference in 1995, Sister Mary Jean asked all of the entities to apply for their respective statewide quality awards and to use the health care self-evaluation criteria as part of their internal system for measuring quality. Our interest was not to win awards, but rather to bring the rigor of a well-regarded self-evaluation process to all of our organizations.

To add the spirit of a challenge to the request, Sister Mary Jean, at that leadership gathering, declared that by 1999 the entire SSM Health Care System would be prepared to apply for the the Baldrige Award. In issuing that challenge, we weren't as enamored of winning an award as we were inspired by the level of quality at which we would have to be operating if we were to do so.

At the end of August 1996, we rolled out the Baldrige Award criteria systemwide, with a full evaluation and education support process. We asked the whole system to organize its operations around the criteria.

The Baldrige Award criteria allow an institution to look across the entire spectrum of its processes. The framework and scoring guidelines of the program, similar to those used in business and industry, provide our health care facilities with a rigorous path to follow. It allows institutions to design and invent their own measuring tools, techniques, systems, and starting points. Each entity chooses who works on what and decides how to organize the self-evaluation. This process encourages creativity and flexibility in adapting the framework to an organization's particular size, activities, and structures.

Between an entity's own self-assessment and the scoring by the objective outside team, each facility gains two diagnostic assessments on 28 results-oriented requirements. The assessments highlight both the strong points and the places that most need improvement.

There are seven key areas for evaluating improvement: leadership, information and analysis, strategic planning, human resource development and management, process management, organizational performance results, and the focus on and satisfaction of patients and other stakeholders.

These seven areas correlate with the core values and concepts of the Baldrige Award—values that very much parallel the system's values. The Baldrige Award values are patient-focused quality and value, leadership, continuous improvement and organizational learning, employee and health care staff participation and development, management by fact, results orientation, community health and public responsibilities, partnership development, design quality and prevention, a long-range view of the future, and fast response to needs.

Just as when we launched CQI, we considered it vitally important to have reference to core principles and values in undertaking self-evaluation. Without them we would have no real purpose, no matter how good our day-to-day evaluations might be.

A major advantage of the Baldrige Award criteria is the demand it places on each of our facilities to have a process for exchanging information throughout the system, to and from the corporate office, and between and among the entitities. The framework of the Baldrige Award criteria assists us in doing this consistently. It calls for us to listen for value and to accept and acknowledge that others outside of our locations have something to contribute to our operation.

## STATEWIDE QUALITY ACHIEVEMENTS

Within little more than a year of being asked by Sister Mary Jean to apply for statewide quality awards, two of our entities received their states' highest quality recognitions: The Missouri Quality Award and the Oklahoma Quality Award, both patterned after the Baldrige Award.

St. Francis Hospital and Health Services in Maryville and Bone & Joint Hospital in Oklahoma City were honored in 1996 for excelling in bringing the principles of quality improvement to their facilities. The recognition was for quality leadership, commitment to customer satisfaction, and continuous improvement of products and services.

Just weeks before the Missouri award was announced, we had talked with Ray Brazier, former president at St. Francis and now president of the system's Hillcrest Health Center in Oklahoma City. St. Francis had made significant strides in quality improvement during Ray's tenure, and we wanted his feedback on what had worked during the first years of CQI implementation there.

When CQI first started in the system in 1990, St. Francis, with a staff of about 320, was experiencing problems with morale, finances, and medical staff relations. The Maryville hospital had many long-time employees who had worked hard through the years to keep the small facility open. There was an obvious commitment to make the hospital work, but something new was needed to improve morale and performance and to build the hospital's reputation in the system and in the community.

It seemed to the president, who had moved there in late 1989, that CQI presented an excellent way to make the difference. He volunteered St. Francis as one of the first six entities to go through the readiness screens and implement quality improvement teams. At first, Ray told us, the leadership and employees expressed a skeptical reaction, as though CQI would be a passing fad. They began the first three teams with mixed success—one worked well, one was okay, and one did not do well.

This was a crucial moment both for the president's leadership and for CQI. Ray allowed no option of giving up or letting CQI quietly fade. He added more teams and increased communication. Before any team started, the president met with the team members and talked with them about why the team was created, what its constraints were, how it fit into the strategic plan, and how it would help in the future. In semiannual meetings with all of the employees, Ray told people what was being measured and why.

When the teams started growing beyond the first three, interest went beyond politeness and started snowballing. Employees began to see that they could actually solve problems, have better communication, and work as a team. Most of the time their proposed solutions would be okayed without any delays. They started saying, "This works."

Ray also found that having people use the measurement and analysis tools as soon as they learned them was the best way to educate. When employees moved through CQI team training and had no team to work on, they lost enthusiasm and knowledge. The team training became just-in-time training so that employees were able to practice with the tools immediately and build up their skills.

Also, the president asked the management team members to go through the team leader training even if they weren't leading a team. As a result of what they learned, the managers started to prepare their own data and analyze it according to CQI techniques.

At the time, Bill Thompson was the central region vice president. He coached Ray in using objective 1E from the existing strategic planning document. The objective asked each department to state its purpose, its role in improving quality, what its customers' needs were and how it knew what they were, and how well it was meeting those needs and how it knew that.

Each month, Ray would have two or three department managers report on their responses to those questions. At first the managers would give elementary answers, but after a while they realized that every time they reported Ray would ask them for data to back up what they were saying. He would say, "What is your source?" As a result, the managers started to measure patient satisfaction and to measure the financial parameters of their departments much more keenly. Ray would have one or two managers report at every board of trustees meeting, which raised the gradient on their reporting even more. Then the managers started reporting successes each month to the medical staff.

From time to time, managers would approach Ray and ask him to give them a break on objective 1E. They would say, "Do we really have to do that?" The president would tell them, "Folks, you might get sick of my saying this, but get your objective 1E done and be prepared to report next month."

Ray said his tenaciousness was one of the most important things in altering people's way of working. Another important ingredient was being willing to learn from others and to involve them.

Still, Ray told us that a shortcoming St. Francis experienced, like other hospitals in the system, was insufficient medical staff involvement. The physicians who become involved have to be genuinely interested and willing to drive the effort among other physicians as well as the entire staff.

Now at Hillcrest, with twice as large a staff as at St. Francis, Ray told us that he is speeding up the improvement process in every area.

Department managers measure not only financial parameters, but also the timeliness and the error rate of their most important process. The managers' monthly reports aren't scheduled such that individuals know when to prepare; rather, they are scheduled at random so that managers have to be prepared every month.

CQI teams are not asked to dot every *i* and cross every *t* of the seven-step model, but rather to follow the main steps of the model. The mission statements for each team are designed more carefully before the team begins, so that the problem is pin-pointed better and fewer meetings are required to design the solution. And realistic time frames of two months, three months, or six months are given in the mission statement so that work moves more urgently.

## CONTINUOUS IMPROVEMENT IS THE UNENDING PURSUIT

We can understand the pitfall of complacency that quality award–winning companies describe. The nature of continuous quality improvement is that you are never finished. There is always something that can be done better. Although it would be a great acknowledgment to be recognized as a national quality award winner, from a practical standpoint, coming *very close* to the top honor might be the ideal.

We do not consider the Baldrige Award criteria to be the last word on how to measure our performance. We view it, rather, as a foundation for developing greater mastery in the discipline of measurement for the purpose of learning what to work on next.

The field for inventing health care quality measures is still in its infancy. The St. Louis Healthcare Alliance is a beginning for area-wide quality measurement, but it is in a very early phase and there are many problems in terms of its reliability. However, it is the best we have now.

The whole industry is questioning, "Can we truly measure quality?" and "How do we use the data to make decisions?" Our system management team is grappling with what it wants to measure. We have a systemwide information system in place that has the capacity to collect all kinds of data. But we are asking, "Who needs the data?" "What are we going to do with it when we have it?"

It takes real thinking to make the transition from raw data to useful information. We have to be committed to making planning decisions based on what we've measured, not simply having one more page of statistics. We need to do a much better job of saying what the key components of success are, how to measure them, and how often to measure them.

We are in a critical place in our own system's history. We have achieved some pioneer accomplishments in the area of quality improvement. We have implemented CQI systemwide. We have positioned education as the foundation of quality improvement. We have brought quality principles to systemwide strategic and financial planning.

This progress, however, is still more or less built on the topsoil of quality improvement. The major accomplishment of the cultural transformation, which is still to come, will be the integration of measurement into all of our services. When we have done that, we will have put quality into our everyday work. Quality improvement will be the way we work here.

........................................

*The Malcolm Baldrige National Quality Award criteria will serve as the fuel for the SSM Health Care System's continuous pursuit of excellence.*

## Note

1. Peter Senge, *The Fifth Discipline* (New York: Doubleday Currency, 1990), 333.

**9**

# VISION OF A NEW CULTURE

*The vague discontent of that May day in 1990, is no longer vague. In seven years of work with CQI, we are clearer about what we are after: the unending pursuit of excellence. The process is everything.*

At the 1990 May leadership conference, Sister Mary Jean led us on a visionary tour of a future SSM Health Care System. No one realized at the time she presented that verbal journey that it would be the foundational vision of a transformed culture—a

177

culture of continuous improvement in the quality of our care and service.

The new culture is still under construction, seven years later. And, frankly, we see no end of the building in sight. In the past several years we've grown larger, stronger, and more complex. We're involved in partnerships and collaborations we couldn't have foreseen. We didn't know much then about integrated delivery networks or the coming influx of managed care companies, especially all those that would be traded on Wall Street.

We weren't focused on downsizing, unionizing, physician partners, or the impetus for healthier communities. If we knew about these things at all, we didn't know their implications.

Even with a strong vision for the future, we could not predict the future. But we've learned that being able to predict isn't nearly so important as being able to envision. Our vision has the power to wrap itself around new, unforeseen forms of service and ministry.

With all of the changes of the past seven years, nothing has shaken our confidence or our constancy of purpose for continuous quality improvement. That isn't to say it has always been fun or easy. Sometimes it has been no fun at all. And we've had to remind one another sometimes why we were doing it.

We have referred in earlier chapters to many people who have helped to advance our cultural transformation by their way of working. It might be tempting to think that after this long we could rely on the momentum they have generated, or the successes we have had, to keep the system progressing in the direction of our vision.

But something we have learned is that the transformation only occurs when it is in process. If it stops, it stagnates. That is why we always keep that future vision of CQI in front of us (see Figure 9.1).

As we have visited other institutions and participated in quality management conferences, we have heard about the companies and

Here, in the SSM Health Care System, all of us work with the conviction that whatever we're doing can always and must always be improved.

We look to the design of a process or the absence of a process to discover why and where the defects exist.

Everyone who works here is seen as a compassionate and intelligent individual who has energy, ideas, and a desire to serve others.

We ensure quality in everything by continually analyzing and improving our processes.

Those who are familiar with a specific process are the ones who collect the data and apply their CQI tools to correct what isn't working.

We solve problems and improve processes without regard for traditional, artificial departmental boundaries.

Our customers and our suppliers are our partners, establishing long-term relationships with us because they have a stake in the quality of the care and service we provide.

In our relationships with coworkers we support each other in doing excellent work all of the time.

**Figure 9.1.** CQI future vision statement.

organizations that tried to bring CQI into their environments and failed. The specific reasons given for failure might be a change of leadership, a lack of sufficient training and education of employees, or an unwillingness to use the quality tools and techniques. But beneath those different explanations is one they have in common: The prevailing culture held on tightly and eventually won out.

There is a real struggle going on between two worlds, between two ways of working. That is why we believe it takes all of our executives, managers, and employees—in every corner of the organization—to embody Deming's "constancy of purpose."

We have been blessed with talented leaders at all levels. For the system to benefit fully from their leadership requires that more of us who are in positions of authority or management recognize them and find more ways to develop and deploy their talents.

This has already occurred with some of our CQI instructors who emerged from less visible positions to become excellent teachers. Similarly, others have come into their own as CQI team leaders and facilitators. Several of the St. Louis Health Care Network's planning team members for functional and clinical integration have emerged as leaders in their facilities as a result of their experience working on that complex project.

As our new culture takes stronger hold, we envision an organization filled with leaders—people who embody excellence and quality and who generate the room for other people to do their jobs with excellence and quality.

With the integration of clinical and functional areas happening across our institutions in several communities, the system's need for managers will decrease. Thus, in cultivating leaders we are not envisioning them becoming managers, but providing leadership wherever they are.

One of the new challenges for those who are in management is to define their role less as a director and supervisor and more as a mentor and coach. Leaders in the new culture are those who have the capacity to call forth others' leadership qualities and allow them to flourish as leaders and contributors in their current jobs.

Leaders provide their leadership by posing the question, issuing the challenge, and tapping the wealth of intelligence, creativity, and courage that people in their departments bring.

Leaders raise the stakes for quality improvements to a high enough level that employee-leaders produce breakthrough results with urgency and energy.

In the new, transformed culture, the system's *organizational* structure remains visible and operative, but it is not the focal point. In the new culture, the *leadership* structure is a circle. Patients and other customers are in the center and managers and employees surround them, learning and working side by side to provide ever-improving products and services.

The SSM Health Care System has won quality awards; we've acquired hospitals and other institutions; we've created integrated delivery networks. Each accomplishment still must bring with it the question, "How do we improve?" For example, how do we operate an excellent integrated delivery network? How do we successfully bring payors and providers under one roof?

One thing we've learned about creating a new culture is that we not only have to speak the vision of how it *will* be, we also have to look inside the existing culture to see how it *is*. With the tools we have, we now can see better where the defects exist and where the gaps are. Such sight will help us as we move into the new millennium.

In the SSM Health Care System of 1990, the tradition of the chain of command still held sway. Few would have spoken publicly against the ideals of innovation and improvement, shared leadership, and listening to employees. But the system had succeeded *without* those ideals being embedded in the organization. It would have been futile to expect a cultural transformation without getting to the roots of what was there.

## DRIVING FEAR OUT OF THE WORKPLACE

The aspects of the culture that can undermine its transformation are the attitudes and ways of operating that managers and employees have the most difficulty bringing to the surface. They are the habits we're attached to, the things we're afraid to say, or the ways of being that are so much a part of the accepted way of operating that we cannot even see them.

In a leadership workshop among system management team members and 13 hospital presidents, we created characteristics of a future reality and then listed aspects of the current reality. An item on the future reality list was "Leadership strives to eliminate fear." A related current reality was "Leadership drives fear into the system."

Committed to learning what could be done about the current reality, we created a task team to define the causes of fear in the organization and create an action plan. Part of the plan was confidential interviews with these 24 senior executives, conducted by consultant and coauthor of *Driving Fear Out of the Workplace*[1] Kathleen Ryan.

In the 60- to 90-minute interviews, several comments were made about Sister Mary Jean's own style of leadership and management. As the CEO and president, she decided to address the issues raised in a face-to-face session with the system leaders. The intention was to begin creating a climate of greater understanding, freedom, and trust, as well as to demonstrate qualities of risk taking and authenticity that could help leaders reduce fear in their own institutions.

Shortly after this, Bill went through a similar process with the people who work with him, allowing them the opportunity to communicate barriers in their interactions with him. He continues to give the people around him room to provide feedback on his operating style, whether they are a secretary or another member of the system management team.

We asked the senior leaders also to carry out this process by obtaining similar feedback from their peers and subordinates. It was our expectation that the leaders' example would give people room to listen for constructive criticism and learn from others. To the best of our knowledge, many of the entity leaders have yet to carry this out with their staffs. Although we will not require them to do so, we suspect that the building of trust and freedom in their entities will be slowed as long as unspoken or unacknowledged fears remain.

As another aspect of generating trust and freedom in the corporate office, we also have taken on a practice of celebrating mistakes by giving people opportunities to debrief and discuss projects that did not succeed as planned. The idea is that leaders can create an environment in which mistakes or misjudgments don't have to be swept under the rug, but rather can be brought up as a learning opportunity for everyone. While we don't suggest that this is necessarily comfortable, it is our assumption that at least part of the discomfort comes from the unfamiliarity of the process.

We have all learned that some of the best ideas for improvement came from discovering what didn't work at first and why. In a risk-taking, innovative environment, we have to be willing to reveal our mistakes as a way of contributing to the communal wisdom of the institution. Without this information, organizations may well keep making the same mistakes over and over again.

The more practiced we become in freely sharing all aspects of our work and our processes, the more we will be creating a climate of trust and freedom in which others can innovate and take risks. This degree of openness may be daunting at first for executives and managers who grew up in a climate of command and control—but we are convinced that if it doesn't begin with key leaders, it won't begin at all.

There is no formula for how to work in the new culture. Continuous quality in health care, despite what some have feared, leads neither to cookie-cutter processes nor to cookbook medicine.

With its collection of corporate executives, facility administrators, and professional health care providers who have decades of formal education, the system has no lack of academic knowledge, professional training, or analytical skills. We don't disparage this learning. We have called on it again and again in order to survive and succeed in our careers.

Yet in creating a vision of a new culture, we have seen that an excessive dependency on what worked in the past dulls the edge of thinking. Throughout the course of CQI, we have much more often needed the type of learning that increases our capacity to invent from nothing, what Senge calls "generative learning."[2]

The system's exemplars of this kind of learning are the various presidents, COOs, department heads, and team leaders who have been patient enough and open enough to persist with questions that stimulate real thinking on the part of their coworkers. This is the process of cultivating a climate of learning that returns much more on the investment than is expended.

Ironically, we have had conversations with employees in the system who are always thinking of ways to help their community groups and their churches do a better job. Unfortunately, at some point they got the message that that sort of contribution wasn't welcome at work.

This reality underlines the fact that intelligent human beings aren't fooled by principles on paper or by idealistic sayings. If there is no acceptance or even consideration of their ideas for improving the real-life nursing unit, kitchen, lab, or office where they work, people will simply put in their time doing what they are told. Worse, they will also become cynical about invitations from system or entity leaders to express their creativity.

In our CQI courses, we have had frontline managers sincerely question why they should waste time having a team try to find a process improvement when they can quickly solve the problem by themselves. And, inside of an adaptive learning organization, rather than a generative one, this is usually how problems are solved. Nothing new is ever brought to the table. Instead, variations on the tried and true keep getting recycled.

When intelligent individuals and their ideas are welcomed, breakthrough solutions start arising from teams working together rather than from managers who routinely impose "right answers" dictated by their attachment to certainty and safety.

Our vision of what it would be like to work inside of the system's transformed culture is of active learners taking initiative to solve problems or create improvements in processes that impact the quality of their jobs.

The transformation of a culture does not happen because the leaders say it should. It is a day-by-day, sometimes moment-by-moment, commitment to break through the automatic and comfortable ways of working and relating with others.

We have been in system board meetings where we felt ourselves almost hypnotically being drawn into "problem-solving" sessions that were in no way in the domain of trustees or system management.

We have been asked by personnel in the corporate office how to handle issues such as after-hours security at the front door.

We have been with entity presidents who pose questions about labor issues and ask how they should handle them.

We have been asked by nurses, physicians, supervisors, and managers about how they should find the time for themselves or their staffs to attend CQI courses or participate on a team.

These examples haven't been reasons to despair of our vision. They just demonstrate the strong cultural pull to go to some other resource besides CQI in times of difficulty. Justifications to return to the old ways of working come dressed in conventional phrases like "It's just common sense," "If it isn't broke don't fix it," "This is only temporary," "This is a special situation," and "We will use CQI tools when we have more time."

With our system straddling two cultures, the old and new, we realize that our determination to not provide answers and solutions to everyone who asks may sometimes seem unfeeling or uncollegial. Yet if we stand for a learning organization, we cannot compromise the process of learning itself.

Returning to hierarchical, patriarchal/matriarchal ways of operating—no matter under what rationale or motive—still leaves people in the same place. They stay dependent on someone else to solve their problems, take their risks, and essentially rob them of the satisfaction of doing their own thinking.

And there are innumerable places for all of us in the system to be bringing creative thinking. We will need to invent new processes and systems, methods, principles, and tools to really be effective in the expanded arenas in which we are participating.

In an incredibly brief period, we have moved from a group of hospitals, to a system, to networks, physician groups, partnerships, community alliances, and joint operating agreements.

How will we infuse the SSM culture into the four-person physician's offices, spread over wide geographic areas? How do we translate CQI principles and tools into managed care plans? How do we have the spirit of excellence spill over into the community, especially in our relationship with community health providers?

## THE HEALTH OF THE WHOLE COMMUNITY

A future we certainly had not foreseen clearly in 1990 was the movement for healthier communities. While today community health initiatives are a key strategic initiative of our system, back then we barely thought about improving the health of large populations.

Yet CQI and our vision of a future reality have prepared us to make an impact on this new sphere of activity. From the moment we began using the tools of CQI on process improvements, to when we began using the "organization as system" approach to our strategic planning, to the integration of clinical and functional processes in the St. Louis Health Care Network, we've seen the necessity of maintaining a system focus if we are to have any leverage in improving the quality of community health.

Clearly, the ultimate system inside of which all of us are working is the interdependent life of the planet Earth. As a smaller system (of 20,000 or so), we have taken on the commitment to discover the SSM Health Care System's leverage points for improving the health of this larger system.

This is probably the most challenging aspect of building a transformed culture because it offers such a broad arena. The challenge is for each of our facilities to bring disciplined systems thinking to all of the work we do, both inside the walls of our institutions and outside. Each entity's planning from the perspective of an organization as system provides it with accurate information about its own human, financial, and material resources; about the resources of the community; the health status of the community; and the environmental and social conditions that affect the health of the community. With this systemic picture, our entities can find the leverage points for making the most beneficial impact on the health of the community.

Whereas in the old paradigm, hospitals were the focal points for "health" care, in the new paradigm our system entities are partners with all of the other social and government institutions in healing illness and injury and promoting health. Our institutions are not islands of medical technology and last-resort acute care. They are part of the system that interdependently fosters and maintains health.

If there is one primary opportunity for greater creativity on our part, it is as we take part in the health of the whole community. Questions about the health status of our communities bring us face to face with the issues that we usually have not dealt with until they came to our doorsteps. And they are more difficult to address outside of our walls than within them.

As an interdependent part of the system, rather than as the medicator and bandager of the system's casualties, we have to ask what the root causes are of the problems and how we contribute to dealing with the root causes. If each of our institutions is a microcosm of the health of the whole community, then we have more work to do to promote among ourselves community, wellness, education, clean environments, and nonviolence.

## COMMUNITY INVOLVEMENT

Hospitals, by virtue of their importance to a community's health and the imposing quality of their structures, usually are noticed wherever they happen to be. Part of the aura of the hospital, however, has been as an institution set apart—a place with its own noise controls and traffic regulations and that serves as the meeting ground for elite specialists.

Often when hospitals participate in the community, they enter as special guests rather than as equals. Sometimes we have noted that other community organizations are reluctant to participate with a hospital for fear of being dominated. Clearly, fear of domination doesn't bode well for partnerships designed to improve the health of the community.

One of the leaders with many years of experience in the system, Carla Baum, demonstrated her intent to deepen the relationship between hospital and community when she became president of St. Joseph's Hospital in Kirkwood. St. Joseph's was a respected institution in Kirkwood for many years and had been part of the SSM Health Care System for about two and a half years when Carla took over. The hospital already had a local governing board providing feedback regarding its activities. Carla sought to enhance the institution's reach into the community by inviting other civic leaders in

Kirkwood, including the mayor, to form quality improvement committees to look at the whole community's health.

In meeting with other leaders, Carla asks, "What are the five things most important to you?" Through this question, the hospital gains a broader view of the needs beyond the hospital walls and can discover where it might be able to impact those needs in partnership with others who also have the community's well-being at heart.

As our community involvements continue to grow even more numerous and complex, our system will have to deal with the question of how we create partnerships with organizations that may not have embraced our philosophy. How we create joint ventures with organizations that do not share our vision?

## CQI'S VALUE

A question that can rightly be asked of us after our having worked inside of the CQI structure since 1990 is, Would we do it all again if we knew then what we know now?

Anyone who has followed us through the chapters of this book can point to misjudgments and false starts. And it is also true that, while we have had some dramatic successes, we have not yet achieved significant gains in every facility.

With CQI we started with a well-defined and what some would call a rigid process for improvement. Some of the rigidity was necessary; some, in retrospect, was probably overmanagement. We did not focus early enough on results. We did not focus enough on the need for significant, timely improvements. We have not been assertive enough in holding people accountable for constant improvements and for asking people to achieve seemingly unachievable results.

The culture is, indeed, under construction. However, what we have been able to build so far with CQI principles is solid. And perhaps more importantly, without having had those principles in place, we can only shudder to think how we would have progressed through the industry and system changes that have occurred in the last seven years. We have noticed that through these changes and challenges, the structure and tools of CQI have remained as relevant as we believed they would.

In health care there are still more issues to be faced. Complacency and burnout will rise as reimbursements become more problematic, paperwork escalates, costs remain difficult to control, competition stiffens, and specialization and departmentalization create a type of gridlock.

But we are fundamentally more convinced than ever that a successful organization truly commits itself to seeking constant improvement in everything that it does, whatever it does. It can never be satisfied with the status quo. It always has to be learning about itself, its customers, and its environment, then rebuilding itself constantly.

Humanly, we sometimes want to ask, "When can we sit back and relax?" We have to remember that there is no "getting there." We need to celebrate our improvements now and keep moving. This isn't something that people who hear with the ears of the old culture like to hear.

But in the new culture we are building, continuous improvement and continuous progress are the jobs to do. We have to constantly challenge people to do more, to do better, and to think about what else can be improved.

*The SSM Health Care System will always be under construction. It is a culture continuously pursuing excellence—not measuring ourselves against the standard of other health care organizations, but against our own vision that whatever we're doing can always and must always be improved.*

## Notes

1. Kathleen D. Ryan and Daniel K. Oestreich, *Driving Fear Out of the Workplace* (San Francisco: Jossey-Bass, 1991).

2. Peter Senge, *The Fifth Discipline* (New York: Doubleday Currency, 1990), 14.

# APPENDIX

The following material is, for the most part, taken from the SSM Health Care System CQI manual. We include it here as a resource for anyone who may be preparing such a manual or who simply wants to see some of the structures and guidelines we used in implementing CQI.

# ROLE OF MANAGEMENT IN CQI

1. Embrace the principles of CQI by setting examples and using the quality improvement process.

2. Commit to continuous quality improvement. Obtain support and active participation by management at all levels.

3. Seek to meet or exceed the needs and requirements of patients and other internal and external customers by basing improvement efforts on patient (and other customer) satisfaction through teamwork.

4. Participate actively as members of quality improvement teams when appropriate.

5. Use measurable standards that reflect patient and other customer expectations.

6. Eliminate barriers to quality improvement by responding to proposed solutions.

7. Continuously stimulate personnel to improve quality by communicating and celebrating success.

8. Maintain a high level of employee interest in quality through awareness.

9. Make resources available when needed.

10. Implement a systematic approach to problem solving.

11. Make decisions based on facts.

12. Provide input to the entity steering committee in identifying improvement opportunities.

13. Ensure and participate in implementation of solutions.

# ROLE OF EMPLOYEES AND PHYSICIANS IN CQI

1. Attend awareness sessions as provided at each entity.

2. Embrace the principles and practices of continuous quality improvement.

3. Actively participate in implementing improvement actions as appropriate.

4. Participate in the entity's quality improvement teams.

5. Participate in quality in daily work life efforts when they are implemented.

# MANAGEMENT'S COMMITMENT

These are seven commitments that leaders promise to fulfill in order to have quality become part of every aspect of the system.

1. Both clinical and management processes throughout the system will be addressed.

2. There will be management and medical staff support and active participation at all levels of the system.

3. A support structure will exist within each entity to support the involvement of everyone in CQI.

4. A high level of awareness of quality will be created throughout the system to ensure individuals' interest and commitment to quality.

5. Recognition will be given to individuals and quality improvement teams who follow the SSM Health Care System CQI model.

6. Awareness and education programs will develop an understanding of the SSM Health Care System CQI model.

7. Successes of quality improvement teams will be communicated throughout the system. Replication will be encouraged to reduce the effort needed in each entity to study similar processes.

## THE ORGANIZATION STRUCTURE

The entity steering team in each facility consists of the president and vice presidents—known as the administrative council—and a staff physician, who are accountable for the work of the entity quality improvement teams.

The CQI implementation team, as Figure A.1 shows, was established as a support/resource group, rather than as a separate line of accountability. Unlike some resource groups that are made up of lower-level managers or administrative assistants who do all of the work, the CQI implementation team was made up of several members of system management, entity leaders, and the corporate director of quality affairs.

The Quality Resource Center (QRC), located in the corporate office, was added specifically to support both clinical and managerial CQI implementation throughout the system. The center is a clearinghouse of CQI information and reference materials, both from our entities and from other institutions. The materials include books, videotapes, audiotapes, articles, reports, research papers, case studies, speeches, and statistical data from the SSM Data Center.

Traditionally, as with most health care organizations, the system's QA was a separate function. At the beginning of CQI, QA

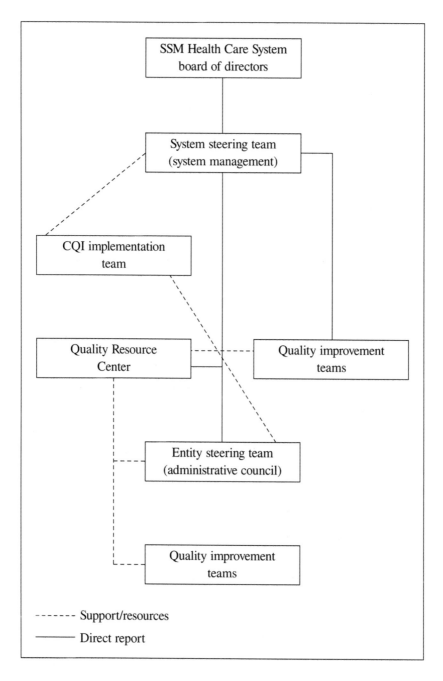

**Figure A.1.** System structure.

continued to be separate from the new Quality Resource Center. This was partly to avoid the appearance of CQI's being merely an addition to the QA department and partly to reduce QA personnel's concern that their jobs would be absorbed by the QRC. Later, QA functions were consolidated into the QRC, the central support for quality care and service throughout the organization.

## ROLES OF THE CQI LEADERS

*The steering team/system management team* from CEO to each vice president had overall and ongoing accountability for CQI. In the manual, we listed 15 specific job responsibilities for this team. Generally, the team's role was to create an environment in which CQI can develop and then to direct the efforts of continuous improvement to ensure quality. The team provides leadership and direction for systemwide implementation of process improvements. The system management team also maintains accountability for all quality improvement teams in the corporate office.

*The CQI implementation team's* role was to serve in an advisory capacity to the system management team. This team developed the overall plan for implementation and was active in initial CQI education efforts.

*Our full-time director of the Quality Resource Center,* located in the corporate office, provides CQI consultation, resource materials, and support to all of the entities and manages the resource center. The director reports to Bill, in recognition of the important accountability the QRC has in the system.

Much of the technical support for CQI comes from the QRC, including assistance on the statistical evaluation of processes, selection of teams, and the system's CQI model. The director also develops, schedules, and provides educational programs related to CQI, including the concepts, tools, methods, and just-in-time training for teams.

*Entity steering teams* lead CQI implementation and monitor results inside of their facilities. An important role is to identify projects for teams to undertake. The early projects were intended to give teams basic experience in the steps of the CQI model. To help promote the involvement of physicians in the CQI effort, we recommended that, even if the medical director was already on the entity steering team, the team also include a practicing physician who was to provide the clinical eyes and ears for administrators and serve as a liaison with other practitioners.

# THE COMMUNICATION PLAN

A large part of building CQI awareness inside the system, especially in the period before all employees could go though the curriculum and work on teams, would depend on our communications tools. We decided to use our existing communication vehicles as one method of disseminating CQI information.

The Quality Resource Center and corporate communications department would provide information for employee newsletters and medical staff bulletins on topics such as course schedules, steps of implementation, and explanations of CQI concepts.

*Network,* the quarterly systemwide newspaper, publishes roundup reports on CQI projects and results from the entities as well as longer educational articles on CQI issues. In every edition of *Network* is a four-page insert called *Quality Chronicle* that is dedicated to in-depth stories on quality-related concepts, tools, or processes, plus feature articles, personal profiles, and Q&A columns.

*Executive Notice* informs corporate and entity administrators about CQI courses and schedules and other learning opportunities.

In addition to using these familiar outlets, the system management team took responsibility for circulating other CQI information from the entities throughout the system.

Entity steering teams would be asked to pass on all appropriate quality improvement team solutions to the system management team, through their respective regional or divisional vice presidents.

Lists of active teams and their projects would be compiled, collated, and circulated every month through the system by the Quality Resource Center. Six-month summaries of projects are also distributed to each entity.

To reach general audiences with information about the system's efforts for continuous quality improvement, we developed a plan employing several avenues.

1. Press releases sent periodically to appropriate media to report on CQI successes

2. Articles for health care/management journals on CQI authored periodically by someone in system management

3. Speeches or panel presentations given by system representatives at regional or national quality conferences each year

4. A minimum of two national or regional CQI conferences attended yearly by system representatives

5. A speakers bureau, made up of volunteers from all levels within the system—including medical staff—for local, regional, or national CQI gatherings

6. Membership in quality associations

# THE READINESS SCREENS

1. Assess the quality environment to determine the organization's readiness to change, resource capability, and commitment to begin implementation of CQI. This screen includes a three-hour educational program called Introduction to CQI.

2. Conduct a baseline employee attitude survey to discover employees' perceptions of how CQI principles are manifested in the respective entity.

3. Select a facilitator to work with the entity steering team. The facilitators would come from inside the steering team and would be trained by members of the CQI implementation team to work with the QITs on their projects.

4. Complete CQI readings and discussion questions. Discuss the results of the questions with system management.

5. Participate in sequential education and training programs: a one-day team member training course (all); 2¹/₂-day administrative council training course (all); five-day team leader training courses (some); and five-day facilitator training courses (some). The entire entity steering team would complete the day-long course (SSMHCS CQI 101) and the administrative council training course, then specified team members and the selected facilitator would take the team leader training (SSMHCS CQI 301) and facilitator training (SSMHCS CQI 401).

6. Select just-in-time training to improve a process that steering team members actually use in their work.

7. Develop a CQI implementation plan for the entity, which includes selection of three CQI projects and establishment of a one-year budget for initial projects and further CQI implementation by the entity.

8. Confirm readiness and receive approval from the system management team to proceed with full CQI implementation.

## THINGS TO CONSIDER REGARDING READINESS SCREENS

Some of the issues that we asked the entity steering teams and their respective regional/divisional vice presidents to consider as practical gauges of the entity's stability and preparedness to undertake CQI (readiness screen 1) were the following:

- Good morale in the entity, especially relative to change
- Lack of major layoffs or cost reduction programs
- Lack of major organizational changes
- Lack of major medical staff problems
- Awareness of significant benefit of implementing CQI
- An understanding among managers that too much time is spent putting out fires

The following is a list of the first six projects taken on by the piloting entities.

1. Cardinal Glennon Children Hospital, St. Louis: The process of updating hospital policy
2. Good Samaritan Regional Health Center, Mt. Vernon: The process of routing documents from the president
3. St. Mary's Hospital, Blue Springs (no longer in our system): The process of meeting photocopying needs
4. St. Marys Hospital Medical Center, Madison: The process of selecting themes and teams for the QITs

5. St. Francis Hospital, Maryville, MO: The process of analyzing how telephones are answered in the administrative areas

6. Corporate office, St. Louis: The process of routing information to the members of system management

# THE DESIGN OF THE QITS

There are five to eight people on each of our quality improvement teams—a mix of employees, managers, and possibly physicians. They may work in a single department or in various departments, but all must be directly involved with the same process. For example, a unit secretary, RNs, LPNs, and CNAs from the same nursing unit might have as their project the improvement of patient response time. Or a project to reduce operating room preparation time might include personnel from the OR staff, the laundry, sterile supply, and housekeeping.

The teams, assisted by a facilitator, meet on a recommended schedule of once a week for one hour. Other time is spent individually on data gathering and preparation. The themes for improvement are assigned by the steering teams. We decided early in CQI planning that teams would not deal with issues regarding regulatory matters, human resource issues (such as pay, promotion, or discipline), or any problem beyond a team's area of competence.

# ROLES ON THE TEAM

## Facilitators

The CQI facilitators come from among the staff of the entity. Our facilitators have three major responsibilities in supporting teams:

(1) providing training in CQI concepts and methods; (2) helping teams solve issues involving the group itself, for example, working together, listening, dividing tasks; and, (3) advising the team on the application of our CQI model and the appropriate tools to use.

As the entities organized for CQI, the administrators usually knew whom they wanted to consider as facilitators. The CQI manual suggested a number of characteristics to guide facilitator selection. The fundamental trait on which all the others build is the belief that quality problems usually are the result of processes rather than bad intentions or incompetence on the part of people. This principle, as we have noted, goes to the heart of CQI.

We expect facilitators to be able to

- Speak clearly and comfortably in public
- Organize and present ideas logically
- Respond confidently to questions, even confrontational ones, in front of a group

As guidelines, we recommended that facilitators possess the following personal characteristics.

- An understanding of organizational politics
- A sense of how and why people act as they do
- An ease with diverse people
- Comfortableness with conflict
- Patience and the ability to listen
- Enthusiasm for and increasing knowledge of CQI
- Energy
- Ability to master technical material
- Some experience or training in management sciences, mathematics, or statistics

- Leadership skill and experience

- Success in working with others to accomplish a goal

- Coaching skill

- Persuasiveness

- The self-assurance to let others take credit for success

In their roles as facilitators, individuals were asked to commit at least 20 hours a week for a year. Their work at team meetings involves

- Assisting the team in going though the steps of the CQI model

- Providing just-in-time training in the processes and tools needed for the team's work

- Guiding the team, when necessary, by recommending the next steps

Between meetings, the facilitators

- Keep all areas informed of CQI activities

- Stay current on the status of teams

- Make use of the Quality Resource Center

- Help the team leader set agendas and prepare for meetings

- Recommend to the leader the use of specialists or experts

- Share the experiences and results of other QITs with the leader

- Critique each meeting with the leader afterward

- Provide guidance and assistance to management in implementing CQI

## Team Leader

In keeping with the fact that everyone on a QIT is considered equal, regardless of background or title, a team leader would not necessarily be the ranking member.

The entity steering team would select leaders based on the personal characteristics and abilities that fit the profile, rather than their position. For the early leaders, we recommended that individuals who had attended our January 1990 hands-on healers gathering be selected because they already had some slight training in CQI and had already demonstrated enthusiasm and leadership.

Preparation for the leader's job includes a five-day team leader training that provides the individual with the knowledge and skills he or she needs to fulfill the role. The leader's tasks are to

- Schedule team meetings and prepare the agenda with the facilitator
- Conduct the meetings according to the agenda
- Communicate and coordinate with the facilitator before and after meetings
- Function as an equal, decision-making member of the team
- Lead the QIT through the CQI model as it works on the project
- Teach and review the CQI tools and techniques as needed at team meetings, with assistance from the facilitator
- Be aware of and monitor the team's involvement and enthusiasm
- Keep all team members involved
- Keep the diverse team members working together
- Communicate with the entity steering team on team results

As with the facilitators, there are some personal characteristics that we recommended for the team leaders.

- Good interpersonal skills
- Competence in their job

• Respect of peers and associates

• Good communication skills

• Positive interest in CQI

• Some previous team experience (if possible)

• Good speaking and presentation skills

• Enthusiasm and energy

## Team Secretary

We recommended that this role be rotated among the team members. Besides participating as an equal member of the team, the secretary prepares and distributes the minutes, including major discussion topics, conclusions, and action items. The secretary also maintains the storyboard that illustrates the team's journey from week to week.

## Team Members

All members on a CQI team were expected, first of all, to agree to carry out the project according to the SSM Health Care System seven-step CQI model. Further responsibilities are to

• Attend all of the meetings

• Actively participate and commit the necessary time for data collection, analysis, and other activities

• Gather and analyze data

• Participate in recommending and/or implementing solutions

• Track the effectiveness of the solutions

• Share experience and knowledge

# INDEX